Musical PUZZLES *of note*

VOLUME II

by Victor Sazer

A BOOK OF:
- Crosswords
- Wordsearches
- Scrambles
  AND MORE!...

ABOUT:
- Musical Terms
- Composers
- Instruments
  AND MORE!

ofnote

Copyright © 1989 by Victor Sazer
All rights reserved.

Portraits of composers: 7, 15, 22, 31, 40, 46,
52, 57, 63, 68: Alan Katz

Art and Book Design: Tony Gleeson

Woodcuts from: Harter, Jim, Music
Dover Publications, NY, 1980

Library of Congress Catalog Card Number: 87-91979
ISBN: 0-944810-01-2

Thanks to my dear wife Betty for her
help, devotion, forbearance and invaluable
proofreading. Thanks to my son Marc for
sharing the eyestrain of proofreading.
Thanks to John Barcellona for a couple
of prize "Sillies."

V.S.

Published by:
OFNOTE
P.O. Box 66760
Los Angeles, California 90066

Printed in the United States of America

FOR ALL AGES

For what age group is MUSICAL PUZZLES OF NOTE? We have been asked this question since publication of the first volume.

Among students and teachers, the first volume was so enthusiastically received at all levels, from elementary though college, that it appears to be enjoyed at all ages. After all, Beethoven is Beethoven whether one is 8 or 80.

Puzzles are fun. STUDENTS, MUSIC LOVERS and PUZZLE BUFFS enjoy the stimulating challenge of puzzles while enhancing their musical knowledge and becoming more "music literate".

This second volume, also, is designed, to allow for the puzzles to be done at TWO DIFFERENT LEVELS, as follows:

1. THE EASIER WAY: First do the WORDSEARCH which precedes each CROSSWORD or SCRAMBLE. The WORDSEARCH contains the words used in the puzzle which follows. This helps you become familiar with the words in advance. You may also use the WORDSEARCH word list for hints when doing the corresponding CROSSWORD or SCRAMBLE.

2. THE MORE CHALLENGING WAY: Do the CROSSWORD or SCRAMBLE first.

Enjoy!

A glossary of musical terms may be found in the back of this book.

ABOUT THE PUZZLES

1. WORDSEARCHES
2. CROSSWORDS
3. SCRAMBLES
4. NOTABLE STORY
5. MYSTERY PICTURES

1. The **WORDSEARCHES** list words which are hidden in the grids of letters. Circle each word. The words may be found forward, backward, going up, down or on a diagonal. Every word is in a straight line with no spaces or hyphens shown in the puzzle. If a phrase of more than one word is used, the space or hyphen between the words will be omitted in the puzzle. EXAMPLES: If the word list shows "PIU MOSSO", it will be found in the puzzle as "PIUMOSSO." "RIMSKY-KORSAKOV" will appear as "RIMSKYKORSAKOV."

2. The **CROSSWORDS** clues will suggest the answers to be filled into the blank spaces of the puzzle.

3. The **SCRAMBLES** are anagrams. The letters of the words are mixed up. Unscramble them and discover the words. As the individual words are found, a surprise message will appear in the in the double lined columns.

4. The **NOTABLE STORY** is a music reading game. Place the names of the notes on the corresponding dashes and the story will emerge. IF YOU DO NOT READ MUSIC, see the key on page 62.

5. Name the composer in each **MYSTERY PICTURE!**

The answers to all puzzles begin on page 69

MUSICAL BUILDING BLOCKS

```
Q  T  T  N  Y  Z  M  Z  S  B  G  X  I  M  L  H
O  S  H  S  I  X  T  Y  F  O  U  R  T  H  E  Z
E  I  I  I  J  N  H  A  L  F  N  O  T  E  S  N
L  F  R  X  R  A  X  R  A  E  X  E  A  D  I  P
U  I  T  T  P  T  T  H  I  R  D  S  L  O  X  W
K  T  Y  Y  S  U  Y  C  R  O  Z  I  F  S  T  A
O  P  S  F  H  R  M  S  U  E  Q  X  E  E  E  G
D  M  E  O  T  A  D  B  E  T  D  T  L  I  E  M
J  P  C  U  X  L  L  A  S  C  O  E  B  G  N  Q
R  M  O  R  I  E  G  T  R  N  O  E  U  H  T  O
D  R  N  T  S  G  E  E  E  C  H  N  O  T  H  F
P  E  D  H  I  L  T  L  P  Z  T  D  H  A  U
G  L  A  S  P  R  O  A  R  T  U  H  H  S  L  V
M  R  R  I  A  H  V  H  A  T  O  S  X  G  F  M
P  W  R  U  W  E  K  D  U  S  K  H  H  A  I  R
H  T  Q  B  S  R  B  L  Q  C  H  Z  J  G  A  E
```

WORDS IN THIS PUZZLE

DOUBLE FLAT
DOUBLE SHARP
EIGHTH
EIGHTHS
FLAT
HALF
HALFNOTES
NATURAL
OCTAVES
QUARTER
QUARTERS
SHARP

SIXTEENTH
SIXTEENTHS
SIXTHS
SIXTYFOURTH
SIXTYFOURTHS
THIRDS
THIRTYSECOND
THIRTYSECONDS
TRIPLETS
WHOLE
WHOLENOTES

ANSWER on page 69

3

MUSICAL BUILDING BLOCKS

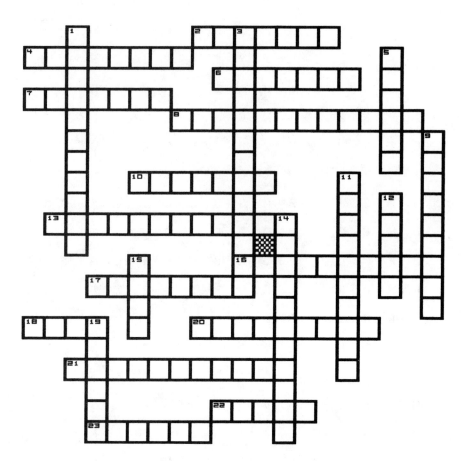

ACROSS

2.

4.

6.

7.

8.

10. ♪ rest

13. 𝄾 rest

16. ♭♭

17.

18. ♭

20. 𝄾 rest

21. 𝄾 rest

22. ♯

23.

DOWN

1.

3.

5. ✔ rest

9.

11.

12. ▬ rest

14. 𝄪

15. ▬ rest

19.

ANSWER on page 69

4

BASIC SEARCH

```
Q  D  N  T  B  N  U  Y  R  J  N  D  I  C  I
E  S  X  E  E  L  J  E  L  R  O  A  O  A  U
I  Y  A  P  O  E  T  B  K  A  I  N  D  N  X
R  A  R  P  E  G  G  I  O  R  T  T  Q  O  H
N  K  T  K  I  A  S  E  I  R  O  I  V  N  C
L  M  I  F  B  T  H  R  A  S  M  R  C  B  H
N  B  C  U  G  O  S  R  U  O  L  Y  T  E  O
M  I  U  O  L  X  Y  Y  K  V  E  F  C  A  R
R  H  L  S  U  M  W  D  T  C  L  L  G  D  D
X  A  A  Q  O  N  S  O  P  P  L  T  A  G  X
T  R  T  T  S  V  T  L  B  E  A  D  G  C  F
T  M  I  M  R  E  A  E  D  X  R  A  U  F  S
O  O  O  T  Y  I  C  M  R  P  A  B  Y  T  H
N  N  N  S  E  P  C  L  H  P  P  J  Q  R  T
E  Y  S  J  H  S  A  Z  P  S  O  H  X  G  B
V  T  J  T  N  J  T  R  S  T  R  I  A  D  I
E  X  M  E  P  S  O  S  N  V  X  C  N  V  L
L  I  U  W  J  F  K  O  J  K  H  P  B  T  A
```

WORDS IN THIS PUZZLE

ARPEGGIO
ARTICULATION
BEADGCF
CANON
CHORD
CODA

CONTRARY MOTION
COUNTERPOINT
FCGDAEB
HARMONY
LEGATO
MELODY

PARALLEL MOTION
RECITAL
SCALE
STACCATO
TONE
TRIAD

ANSWER on page 69

NOTABLE BASICS

ACROSS

3 Tones of a chord played one note at a time
5. Order of flats in key signatures
8. Two or more musical lines moving in opposite directions
12. Stepwise progression of notes
13. Three tone chord with a root, a third and a fifth
14. Musical combination of tones
15. Ending section
16. Harmonic combination of two or more tones.
17. Sound of recognizable pitch

DOWN

1. Separated abruptly
2. Smooth and connected
4. Two or more musical lines moving in the same direction
6. Distinctness and character of execution
7. Round
8. Two or more musical lines performed at the same time
9. Tune
10. Order of sharps in key signatures
11. Concert by one or several performers

ANSWER on page 69

NAME THE MYSTERY COMPOSER #1

Born: Votkinsk, Russia
    May 7, 1840

Died: St. Petersburg, Russia
    Nov. 6, 1893

* Had a tragic life of emotional and psychological problems.

* Studied law and worked for three years as a clerk at the Ministry of Justice.

* His patroness, Nadezhda von Meck, supported him for thirteen years so he could compose.

* Eugene Onegin   * Pathetique Symphony

* Swan Lake   * Nutcracker Suite

ANSWER on page 69

SEARCH IN GOOD FORM

```
E  U  G  I  G  I  H  W  Q  B  E  F  V  C  D  I  Z
L  C  U  Q  J  X  U  U  Z  F  E  E  R  U  O  B  U
A  C  O  U  E  L  O  D  N  A  R  A  F  A  O  D  W
Q  B  A  S  A  L  T  A  R  E  L  L  O  L  N  F  L
W  T  F  V  I  I  O  J  A  M  B  E  E  L  O  F  X
T  C  C  W  A  C  L  R  E  T  S  R  H  E  C  Z  D
O  M  O  H  L  T  I  G  A  I  O  Y  A  M  T  Y  T
D  G  W  U  A  L  I  L  A  C  E  J  Z  A  U  G  M
U  J  V  W  R  C  U  N  I  C  R  T  R  N  R  Z  T
T  F  H  K  A  A  O  G  A  E  A  A  T  D  N  B  E
B  N  A  P  Y  L  N  N  Q  D  N  S  B  E  E  Q  U
Y  A  B  R  O  G  T  T  N  T  Z  N  S  H  S  F  N
R  V  A  P  Q  T  E  Z  E  E  D  M  E  A  O  U  I
U  A  N  E  U  G  A  L  A  M  S  Y  T  L  P  A  M
A  P  E  P  M  S  L  J  E  L  M  H  L  K  R  V  U
H  M  R  B  C  A  P  R  I  C  C  I  O  G  S  H  X
M  M  A  Z  U  R  K  A  E  T  A  F  P  W  O  E  Y
```

WORDS IN THIS PUZZLE

ALLEMANDE	FARANDOLE	MUSETTE
BARCAROLE	FOLLIA	NOCTURNE
BOLERO	GIGUE	PASSACAGLIA
BOUREE	HABANERA	PAVAN
CAPRICCIO	HYMN	POLONAISE
CAVATINA	JOTA	SALTARELLO
CHACONNE	MALAGUENA	SICILIENNE
COURANTE	MAZURKA	TARANTELLA
ELEGY	MINUET	WALTZ

ANSWER on page 69

SCRAMBLE #1

AVIANCAT

ZTLWA
NOCHANCE
UGGEI
ALLNEATART
MANUALAGE

OOSPANIEL
RELOADFAN

ANEARBAH
OURBEE
LEANMEDAL
CONTUNER
TUNEMI
GEYEL

IICELINENS
EMUTEST

SPACIALSAGA

TAOJ
ONATRUCE
NMHY

OFLAIL
AREARBLOC
KUZMAAR
LASERATOLL
VAPNA
LEOORB
COPICIRCA

ANSWER on page 69

9

DYNAMICS PLUS

```
O  M  I  S  S  I  S  S  I  T  R  O  F
Q  M  J  Q  L  A  U  E  E  T  R  O  F
P  Y  I  J  H  U  C  U  W  P  J  O  O
F  S  T  S  C  S  R  C  I  M  R  C  R
E  T  N  S  S  Z  L  A  E  T  F  Z  T
O  T  D  I  M  I  N  U  E  N  D  O  I
D  G  R  R  P  I  S  P  X  P  T  G  S
N  S  P  O  S  R  I  S  F  I  Z  P  S
A  A  B  S  F  A  I  K  I  A  T  R  I
Z  G  I  U  N  O  W  A  T  N  Q  M  M
R  M  Z  O  B  D  Z  G  H  O  A  D  O
O  N  A  I  P  O  Z  Z  E  M  D  I  I
F  G  O  D  N  E  C  S  E  R  C  J  P
S  U  T  D  J  A  P  K  M  M  B  R  V
```

WORDS IN THIS PUZZLE

ACCENT
CRESCENDO
DIMINUENDO
DOT
FORTE
FORTEPIANO
FORTISSIMO
FORTISSISSIMO

HAIRPINS
MEZZOFORTE
MEZZOPIANO
PIANISSIMO
PIANISSISSIMO
PIANO
SFORZANDO
SLUR

ANSWER on page 70

DYNAMICS PLUS

ACROSS

4. *p*
5. *fff*
10. *mf*
11. *ff*
12. ⌒
14. *sfz*
15. *fp*
16. ◁

DOWN

1. *pp*
2. *ppp*
3. ◁ ▷
6. >
7. *mp*
8. ◁
9. ·
13. *f*

ANSWER on page 69

SIGNS AND SYMBOLS

```
B  F  E  A  B  A  S  S  C  L  E  F  S  J  G  N  T
H  G  H  F  E  S  N  A  G  I  R  S  T  M  U  J  P
B  Q  F  A  I  M  G  C  L  R  T  Y  A  B  S  E  G
T  I  T  G  T  R  I  L  L  T  T  V  F  M  E  W  M
V  M  N  E  F  X  S  T  W  L  O  A  F  Q  F  V  W
K  J  H  D  X  A  T  T  N  G  U  C  E  O  R  S  N
F  B  A  I  V  H  A  H  E  O  T  U  L  Q  H  G  E
U  E  G  R  S  R  E  M  C  N  M  N  C  E  I  P  F
V  T  O  E  T  D  P  U  E  Q  D  M  R  S  F  E  B
C  U  T  T  I  M  E  D  N  X  L  I  O  U  L  H  D
F  M  O  P  I  V  R  L  R  G  O  T  N  C  T  V  X
O  X  T  H  D  O  F  C  G  Z  O  Y  E  G  M  Q  J
K  G  O  A  M  J  D  F  Z  G  B  L  T  I  A  R  Y
D  N  P  O  D  O  U  B  L  E  B  A  R  I  D  L  P
F  W  F  M  G  B  E  I  Y  E  P  X  J  I  C  X  F
N  N  M  Y  A  G  F  E  R  M  A  T  A  Y  W  Q  F
U  J  H  I  Q  T  Q  T  E  X  V  A  B  Z  K  A  F
```

WORDS IN THIS PUZZLE

ALTO CLEF
BASS CLEF
COMMON TIME
CUT TIME
DOUBLE BAR
FERMATA

FIRST ENDING
GO TO SIGN
GO TO TOP
MORDENT
REPEAT SIGNS
SIGN

STAFF
TENOR CLEF
TREBLE CLEF
TRILL
TURN

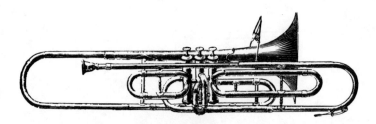

ANSWER on page 70

SIGNS AND SYMBOLS

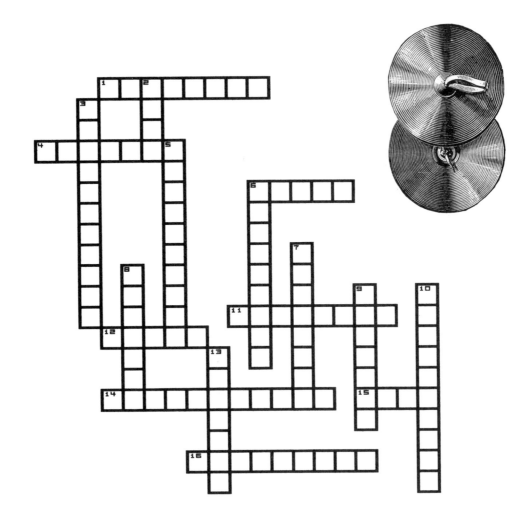

ACROSS

1.

4. ⌒

6. *tr*⌒

11. ⒀

12.

14.

15. ∽

16.

DOWN

2. 𝄋

3.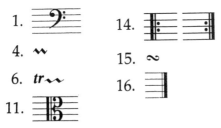

5.

6.

7. *D.S.*

8. ¢

9. 𝄐

10. C

13. *D.C.*

ANSWER on page 69

NOTABLE STORY PART #1

This is a music reading game. Place the names of the notes on the corresponding dashes and the story will emerge. You may read either the upper or lower staff. IF YOU DO NOT READ MUSIC, see the key on page 62.

Continued on page 30

NAME THE MYSTERY COMPOSER #2

Born: Ciboure, France
      March 7, 1875

Died: Paris, France
      December 28, 1937

* Entered the Paris Conservatory at fourteen and became interested in inovative musical techniques.

* Utilized jazz in a movement of his Violin Sonata called "Blues."

* Did the most famous orchestration of Mussorgsky's Pictures at an Exhibition.

* Daphnis et Chloe

* Piano Concerto for Left Hand Alone

* Tzigane   * Bolero

ANSWER on page 70

GERMAN/AUSTRIAN COMPOSERS

```
S  L  C  U  L  K  B  T  N  G  M  H  D  S  T  R  A  U  S  S  A  P
C  A  J  T  G  V  H  B  D  E  L  C  V  F  E  O  R  O  K  W  M  H
N  X  S  X  C  E  Z  A  I  Y  S  U  C  N  L  S  L  C  S  A  N  Y
H  F  K  B  B  R  U  C  K  N  E  R  C  S  E  L  A  T  C  Z  N  S
H  E  F  T  R  E  B  U  H  C  S  B  B  K  M  O  F  I  H  H  N  T
E  E  W  R  B  W  E  U  I  H  N  E  S  U  A  H  K  C  O  T  S  O
O  G  N  A  O  E  G  J  W  M  C  I  E  Z  N  T  O  S  E  F  K  B
I  Z  V  Z  G  M  E  W  O  O  Y  A  D  M  N  O  S  Y  N  A  G  Z
V  A  C  O  E  N  B  T  M  E  L  C  B  R  I  L  W  E  B  E  R  N
R  E  Y  M  R  I  E  I  H  B  R  F  G  T  E  T  F  R  E  M  E  R
J  X  E  E  R  O  N  R  R  O  A  O  J  D  U  P  A  I  R  Z  B  I
L  Y  T  I  L  G  P  A  E  D  V  X  N  R  H  H  M  N  G  A  O  U
N  S  T  A  T  S  I  J  G  E  I  E  N  I  M  A  A  U  T  N  Z  E
H  O  W  F  M  N  N  Y  E  O  M  E  N  S  A  Y  P  N  H  S  N  P
Z  N  S  H  A  Y  D  N  R  P  R  D  O  H  H  V  C  V  D  J  D  F
H  J  O  T  E  R  L  E  A  N  E  S  L  A  L  O  M  X  V  E  N  T
Z  U  V  F  A  N  B  Z  J  M  O  S  O  A  E  W  Y  T  R  I  L  S
H  Y  D  O  R  E  A  X  I  O  U  E  O  S  R  O  U  X  Y  V  V  N
E  Z  S  X  W  S  F  T  A  H  A  H  Q  P  T  M  Y  Q  A  B  A  Q
N  F  X  G  G  P  H  P  S  A  N  C  C  A  E  X  U  K  B  X  M  L
T  M  B  C  Y  A  V  K  X  P  L  A  N  S  X  D  B  W  J  G  X  U
R  O  S  O  R  X  O  V  V  J  J  Z  Z  J  G  C  U  Y  B  I  H  B
```

WORDS IN THIS PUZZLE

ACHE	EON	OR	STERN
ALES	GLUCK	ORFF	STOCKHAUSEN
ANTS	HAHA	ORO	STRAUSS
ANY	HANDEL	OSLO	TATS
AYE	HAY	PLAN	TELEMANN
BACH	HAYDN	PO	TIC
BECOMING	HENZE	RAFT	TIE
BEETHOVEN	HINDEMITH	RAH	TOM
BERG	HUMPERDINCK	RED	TRI
BIRDIE	KANT	REGER	TURNER
BRAHMS	MAHLER	SCHOENBERG	VENT
BRAIN	MENDELSSOHN	SCHUBERT	WAGNER
BRUCH	MOZART	SCHUMANN	WEBER
BRUCKNER	NOR	SLALOM	WEBERN
DEPOSE	OAR	SPA	WHEN
EMIT	OHMS	STA	WOLF
EMU			

ANSWER on page 70

GERMAN/AUSTRIAN COMPOSERS

Match the composers' last names to the first and/or middle names found in this puzzle.

ACROSS

1. _____ I was a lad
3. Horse staple
4. Johannes
7. Alban
9. _____ one for tennis
10. _____ aye, captain
11. Arnold
15. Anton
16. Engelbert
17. Georg Philipp
19. Remove from power
21. Make preparations
24. Cravat
27. Color
29. George Frederick
30. Zigzag ski course
31. Occuring at intervals of three: pref.
32. A very long time
33. Masculine name
35. Rear part of a ship
38. Karlheinz
42. Either
43. Ludwig van
45. Anton
46. Pleasing to the eye
47. Max
49. Water craft
52. A fashionable resort
53. Franz
54. Richard
55. Hurt

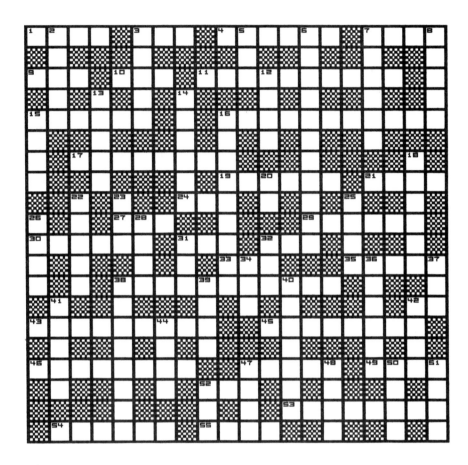

DOWN

2. Hans Werner
3. Franz Joseph
5. Cheer word
6. Felix
7. Badminton need
8. Christoph Willibald
12. Electrical units
13. Max
14. Wolfgang Amadeus
15. Hugo
16. Paul
18. Gustav
20. River in Italy
22. _____ storm
23. Gold: Spanish
25. Colonial insects
26. City in Norway
28. Give off
31. Twitch
32. Large flightless bird
34. Rower
36. Lathe operator
37. And not
38. Robert
39. German philosopher
40. Richard
41. Carl Maria von
42. Carl
44. Air opening
47. Johann Sebastian
48. Happy sounds
50. Pub wares
51. Makes lace
52. Depot. abbr.

ANSWER on page 70

BITS AND PIECES #1

```
T D T M Y N S Q B D E S C C B G S R J C
I S N S R N F Q G D G N X Z L V B R A Y
A E Y V P O O M F R G O I T W A I R J A
R N F M R I Z H O J E B T G W R N T F I
T I Y I P J N U P N O A V G M I A A V B
R P T E N H V E L M P T N I V A N R W T
O S X U V V O T S Y Y I R A I T I P X H
P O C G R O H N P O R S L E A I G S O E
N R J H A I R L I P F O L S C O H D P P
L C I C P O O T S E F R T A R N T Y T L
O H F O H W Z F B T E I O U R S O H I A
C E L R Z A O A H H C S E M N O N C H N
N S O R C E R E R S A P P R E N T I C E
I T O F T O A W Y A S Z A A Y G O S U T
L R D I U N B M E W T B R B N L T O A S
A A R T I F P Q L A R Y T O B O L W P P
K M E M S H M R L F A R M S P I L L S O
A A A H O S E A E U P I F J T N R E B P
Y L X N I A T N U O M D L A B V S N K X
S N Y E T S G B T E N O T M I E O V B A
```

WORDS IN THIS PUZZLE

A LINCOLN PORTRAIT
ALA
ART
ASH
BALD MOUNTAIN
BAR
BARNS
CHAR
CHIT
CONCERTO
CARNIVAL OF THE ANIMALS
ENIGMA
EON
FANTASTIC SYMPHONY
FARMS
FLOOD
FOR
GOT

HAIR
HOSE
III
LYRE
NEO
NIGHT ON
NYETS
ORCHESTRA
PASTORAL SYMPHONY
PINES OF ROME
PLOW
POON
RIB
RID
RIO
RITE OF SPRING
ROUTE

SNOB
SORCERER'S APPRENTICE
SPILLS
SPINES
SPRAT
STIR
STOOP
SYMPHONIE ESPANOLE
THE PLANETS
TIL
TO
TON
TRAP
TROVE
VARIATIONS
YELL

ANSWER on page 70

BITS AND PIECES #1

Find the names of the well known pieces of music suggested by the clues.

ACROSS

1. Unbelievable piece. 2 wds: Berlioz
9. See 45A,21D
11. Musical menagerie. 4 wds: Saint-Saens
14. Bend forward
15. Puzzler. See 23D: Elgar
17. _____ market
18. Tease
20. Evening on hairless hill. 2 wds. See 19D: Mussorgsky
22. From the flame
24. Sesame plant
25. Liquid problem
26. Animal housing
27. Field preparer
28. Russian nos
29. Italian trees. 3 wds: Respighi
30. Superior one
32. Jack _____
33. Creative endeavor
34. Backbones
35. Arouse
36. Line of travel
37. Obtained
38. Roman numeral
39. Chicken _____ king
43. Ancient Greek instrument
45. Solo for the whole assemblage. See 9A,21D: Bartok
46. New. pref.
47. Magician in training. 2wds. Dukas

DOWN

2. Tribute to a U.S. president. 3wds: Copland
3. Valuable find
4. See 25A
5. Tab
6. Hardwood for masts
7. Scream
8. Country scenes. 2 wds: Beethoven
9. Agricultural units
10. Free from
12. Top covering
13. Spanish music from France. 2wds: Lalo
15. Long time
16. Outer space places. 2wds: Holst
17. Heavy weight
18. Post winter ceremony. 3 wds: Stravinsky
19. 2 wds. See 20A
21. See 9A,45A
23. See 15A
31. Prevent
40. Garden need
41. Singe
42. Snare
44. _____ Grande

ANSWER on page 70

19

NOTABLES

```
G E Y H W B I H Z B L R P Z R R D G N G A W F
U E W D O F R A N Z S C H U B E R T V U P Y X
J L O I L Z I X C N N J D M F Z B L K N P S G
J O N R F I R E N G A W D R A H C I R C O C F
H R H X G Q T M B D P M Y Z S I S U D B E N A
V V O A A E L P H C Y Y U L T X Z F H Y E D F
D I S O N L F F A Y C A B H H B E U M V M H P
Z M S X G N D R S P G H H R C K A M O E Z M U
P D L Y A W S C E M N I H H S S D H Y U A Y N
Z U E T M Z O E N D H N U E P S T D R Y R P Q
I I D Q A O P M B P E A T S C E X R R V B W M
L M N C D O E Q P A K R R T E P S Z E V G B X
E X E K E C C Y C A S Q I B R P E O J B G Z B
O K M W U U J C K F D T N C S C P X J O O V W
E J X U S D H M G P M A I K K E O E Y D V R H
V J I P M W Q N Q I V X F A J H N E V M G F X
P F L O O I J B Q G J O Y B N D A N J E K G D
V T E I Z W C S I E L I I T U B L N A A R S R
L E F G A N V W M B Y I E V T V A U D H P D M
P Y X O R T D S N I U O A Z X P F C S E O U I
V D M J T U W X N I W H N G P B V Q H T L J Z
Z C A R L M A R I A V O N W E B E R K U W M S
```

WORDS IN THIS PUZZLE

JOHANN SEBASTIAN BACH

LUDWIG VAN BEETHOVEN

JOHANNES BRAHMS

GEORGE FREDERICK HANDEL

JOSEPH HAYDN

FELIX MENDELSSOHN

WOLFGANG AMADEUS MOZART

FRANZ SCHUBERT

ROBERT SCHUMANN

GIUSEPPE VERDI

RICHARD WAGNER

CARL MARIA VON WEBER

ANSWER on page 71

NAME THESE NOTABLES #1

1. _____

2. _____

3. _____

4. _____

5. _____

6. _____

ANSWER on page 70

21

NAME THE MYSTERY COMPOSER #3

Born: Nelahozeves, Bohemia
    September 8, 1841

Died: Prague, Austro-Hungarian Empire
    May 1, 1904

* Worked in his father's butcher shop as a child.

* Great melodic gift and champion of Bohemian music.

* He was inspired to write some of his best music after hearing Afro-American and Native American music while on his three year stay in the United States.

* Slavonic Dances   * American String Quartet

* New World Symphony

ANSWER on page 70

EXPRESSIVE WORD SEARCH

```
B A L A Z M K I Q B D O L O R O S O P L N M U
H V K I H F B L C A L A N D O D E O J I S A O
W J Z L E G G I E R O O J O D N A L R A P R L
O T A N O I S S A P P A F S R A I W P A B C J
K T Q Z Y B O T U L O S I R A T O T F N A A S
O K A C C E L E R A N D O W L N S B N D S T T
D K R O V I S S E R P S E I L A O A M A J O A
O O P I U M O S S O Q L P A E C I A N N D D C
L D P Q F N V O G U B R R P N U R F Y T P N C
C N T P V S S T Z R Q B E R T C U L P E R E A
E A P B I M I E A G A W S N A V F W L T E G T
X Z L V M O P M R S H Z T T N G X G A R S N O
Q R P L Y E M P F E U F I O D N A D R A T I R
D E O S E A N O C G C S S O O M Q Z G N O R J
S H A X O G C O V M S A S E S J Y U H Q E T D
E C F N P T R O M I S S I C L O D O E U F S A
C S E R I J T O M O M P M P J I N D T I Z I S
C O N F U O C O L F S E O T A O B N T L O H F
O P S J I C Q E V R U S N B W Q C A O L U E I
E C E N E R G I C O T R O T L V M M T O C N Q
W N V I V A C E X D C W I G O Y C L Y N M H J
K R H Y T H M O V H E E M O D E R A T O A E R
F J Y O G R A L N N D G D O S I C E D H C O
```

WORDS IN THIS PUZZLE

ACCELERANDO
ALLEGRO
ANDANTE
ANDANTINO
APIACERE
APPASSIONATO
CALANDO
CALMANDO
CANTABILE
CANTANDO
CON FUOCO
DECISO
DOLCE
DOLCISSIMO
DOLOROSO

DOPPIO MOVIMENTO
ENERGICO
ESPRESSIVO
FURIOSO
GRAZIOSO
LARGHETTO
LARGO
LEGATO
LEGGIERO
LISTESSO TEMPO
MARCATISSIMO
MARCATO
MENO MOSSO
MODERATO
PARLANDO

PIU MOSSO
PRESTISSIMO
PRESTO
RALLENTANDO
RHYTHM
RISOLUTO
RITARDANDO
SCHERZANDO
SECCO
SOTTO VOCE
STACCATO
STRINGENDO
TRANQUILLO
VIVACE

ANSWER on page 71
```
```

SCRAMBLE #2

GALOR

GRINDSTONE
NATIONAND
HOGRATTLE
ANDROIDART
IMOMPOPDEVOTION
LOANCAD

DOCLEARANCE
TEARMOOD
OSPOTLESSITEM
NEATAND
LEARNTOLAND
REALLOG
IMPSSTORIES

SOMEMOONS
MISOSOUP
SEPTOR
ICREEPAA
CAVVIE

BALANCEIT
CZARNOSHED
NICEOGRE

COLDE
LOOSDOOR
MIDSISCOOL
PATOSSAPIANO
ONUFCOCO
IZOORAGS
EATLOG
IROOFUS

COVETSOOT
LAPARDON
NORALLQUIT
TRYHMH

ACOLDMAN
AMACTOR
ROVESSPIES
CATCOATS
ANDNOACT
IROLEEGG
COSEC
SOURTOIL

ISCODE
SITCOMISAMAR

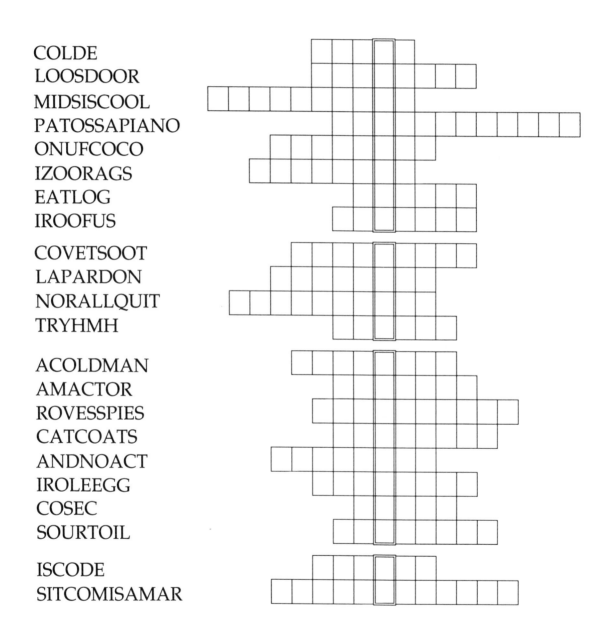

ANSWER on page 71

COMPOSERS OF ITALY

```
S G V R O S S I N I T E Z F V M N M R D F O Y
I N I L L E B Y H H F Y A A O U D Y I E D U I
P B V W L U A J R U C N I L U S E G Z L K T N
L I A Y A L V K O G P B N O S V O S F M C W Z
H D L X V C W T C E N N I T P G Q N E B O X A
C L D E A L A B R I N A C L A R E T R K K K H
R A I A C V E G E L A G C F E L N A A A B F W
A B S W N M O M X L O H U S L A N E P H V T Z
U O T T O L C N L E E W P S L I E B Q T C T R
H C U T E B W G T R E M O R S A A R T T A T M
D S R S L L A Q U O H P M V R T T N Z J E H M
O E I E Z G N B P C C A F G H I L H S L T Y P
B R B R O T I U G A L U I Z R M K W I T Y V L
N F S O L N R Y O I T T E Z I N O D N L I A I
Y K K F I S T F P V T O M P C L R W K V F L N
M A C E K H S I E A O Y Z C F E M U Y F U E L
D A D L R P E O L L G T M F V W Y N E S U G I
Y L S N I R L R B S C H E C K L B T U O Z D X
K L D C O O A E Q Y K R Y D T L Y L A I B D S
E E D F A C P M A S R F K P E Y I U V R A Y H
W S N A S G Q S T A I U E G D S R M U E V A L
O A M X J H N O R S I N I R E H C C O B J M H
V C Z R E S P I G H I B Q A R A R O P R O P W
```

WORDS IN THIS PUZZLE

AGOG	CORELLI	LEONCAVALLO	SCAN
ALL	CUE	LIE	SCARLATTI
ARA	DONIZETTI	LIMO	SLAT
ARCH	ELI	MALIPIERO	SNAIL
ASH	ERR	MASCAGNI	SOB
BATH	ETNA	NOV	SPOIL
BELLINI	FOREST	ORB	SST
BERIO	FRESCOBALDI	OUT	STILL
BOCCHERINI	GAG	PALESTRINA	STOP
CASELLA	INCUR	PERGOLESI	SUL
CASTELNUOVO-	INEPTLY	PORPORA	TI
TEDESCO	INKY	PUCCINI	TREMORS
CHECK	LAVE	RANI	USE
CHERUBINI	LEAPS	RAP	VERDI
CLARET	LEG	RESPIGHI	VIVALDI
CLEF	LEN	ROSSINI	WOLF-FERRARI
CLUE			

ANSWER on page 72

COMPOSERS OF ITALY

Match the composers' last names to the first and/or middle names found in this puzzle.

ACROSS

1. Ottorino
9. Giovanni Pierluigi
10. Cleansing
12. Gian Francesco
14. Motionless
15. Signal
16. Mod gab
18. Ruin
20. Masculine name
21. Exploit
23. View
24. Bring upon oneself
25. Curved structure
26. Hint
28. Giovanni
32. Winter mo.
34. Wash
35. Slow moving mollusk
36. Everyone
37. Highly excited
38. Sol La _____ Do
40. Wilderness
42. Classy car
43. Musical symbol
44. Shakes
46. _____ Whitney
47. Hindu princess
49. Jumps
50. Arcangelo
51. Campfire leftover
52. Strip of wood
53. Make a mistake
54. Girolamo
57. Like a dark liquid
58. At the movies
59. Luigi

DOWN

2. Sicilian volcano
3. Clumsily
4. Mario
5. Vincenzo
6. Sphere
7. Alfredo
8. Cease
10. Luciano
11. Constellation in the Southern Hemisphere
12. Pietro
13. Ruggiero
15. Luigi
17. Giacomo
19. Domenico
22. _____ tasto
27. Ermanno
29. Comic remark
30. Shake a _____
31. Speedy means of transportation
33. Giuseppe
39. Gaetano
41. Niccolo Antonio
45. Antonio
47. Gioacchino
48. Dry red wine
50. Chess move
55. Cry
56. Falsehood

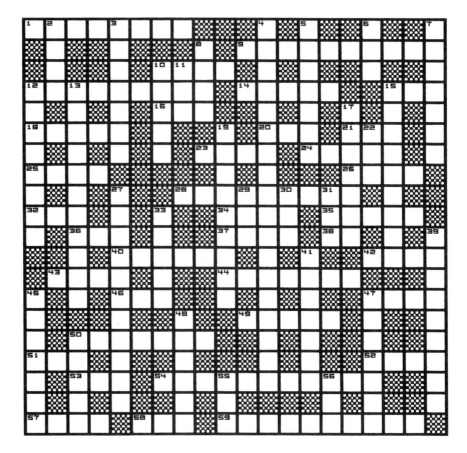

ANSWER on page 72

OPERATIC SEARCH

```
V J J B M Q A R F B O P F Z N J R V Q J A B
O G S A Q H D P M G P I W N U P K H T U L K
A K G R E B M U X A M C R E G O O H W S S Q
V G A D I O L C H M N A E T O M R C Z Y P U
Q N A Z T R J C Q U L S S W G I O G H F N G
U R E I I O O I O O S B E S R R P M F I R L
O T O R N D V N E A T P W W E B G T O X E J
T F I S A I A I V A S E N B U N N R D Y B T
K M F F S N L L V M S I B R K L E Y Q F E L
P O A E E I V L R A T I A R A P R T S N W O
W Z Y S N D N E E Z F A S D E L C P V A I O
E A N K C B V I Z B A S F P E H O R G I P Z
E R E D S A A H N D M I P O A R S N S D L K
Q T E L P G G C O E K C N I D R E P M U H P
Z N K M A Z R N H E V C K U S R F E I M Q V
J C V E R D I O I S A O O N S L T V I P T F
J D M V S Z C P S V V E H P R Q Y Z C S L E
X P S T E B A M A S S M E T A N A D P O N V
E E O T A B N L K X U T T M E N O T T I Q E
Y P T B S R L Y Y Q S M Y N G E R S H W I N
O I Z G G O U N O D N E T T I R B K U Z N X
I M Y Z E T W K S B J Q Z N K M S P S C C L
```

WORDS IN THIS PUZZLE

ABETS	FIR	MUSSORGSKY	SMETANA
ALOE	GERSHWIN	NOUN	STEPS
ARE	GOUNOD	OFFENBACH	STOP
BEETHOVEN	HUMPERDINCK	ORE	TAR
BELLINI	IKE	OVAL	TCHAIKOVSKY
BERG	IN	OWN	TIA
BIZET	LAD	PAVE	TIN
BORODIN	LEONCAVALLO	PICAS	TRIO
BRIM	MASCAGNI	PONCHIELLI	TRY
BRITTEN	MASSENET	PUCCINI	VASE
DONIZETTI	MENOTTI	RAN	VERDI
DROPS	MERE	ROSSINI	VIE
DUMPS	MET	SEWN	WAGNER
ERGO	MINT	SHERBET	WEBER
EVEN	MOM	SIPS	WEE
FA	MOP	SLY	YES
FIBBER	MOZART		

ANSWER on page 72

OPERA

Who wrote the operas named in this puzzle?

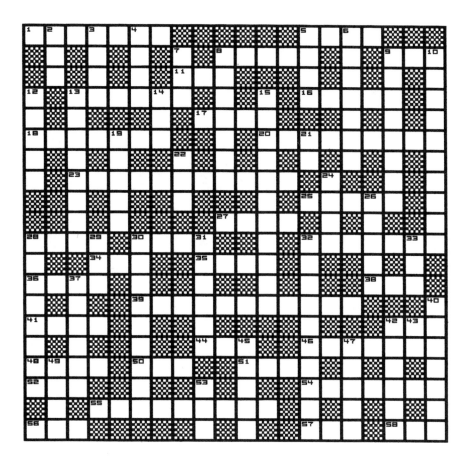

ACROSS

1. The Bartered Bride
5. Tastes
8. Carmen
9. Swab
11. We _____ here
13. Faust
16. Printer's measures
17. Soothing plant
18. Prince Igor
20. Tales of Hoffmann
23. Hansel and Gretel
25. Aida
27. Improve a road
28. Make money
30. Outer edge
32. The Telephone
34. Presidential nickname
35. _____ office
36. Stitched
38. Foxy
39. Eugene Onegin
41. Therefore
42. Tree
44. Aunt in Mexico City
46. The Barber of Seville
48. On a par
50. Contend
51. Wozzek
52. Sailor
54. Sweet dessert
55. Lucia di Lammermoor
56. Understand
57. Affirmation
58. Doubletimed

DOWN

2. Parent
3. Group of a certain size
4. Speech part
5. Come to a standstill
6. Madame Butterfly
7. Young fellow
8. Norma
9. Cavalleria Rusticana
10. La Gioconda
12. Der Freischutz
13. Porgy and Bess
14. Have to keep
15. I Pagliacci
19. Down in the _____
21. Mi _____ sol
22. Mined material
24. Only
26. Rain _____
28. Manon
29. Metal
30. Fidelio
31. The Marriage of Figaro
32. Boris Godunov
33. Give it a whirl
37. Tristan und Isolde
40. Peter Grimes
42. Falsifier
43. Ready for visitors
45. Helps
47. Stairway parts
49. Flower vessel
53. Celebrated opera house: abbr.

ANSWER on page 70

29

NOTABLE STORY PART #2

Continued on page 45

NAME THE MYSTERY COMPOSER #4

Born: Lucca, Italy
     December 23, 1858

Died: Brussels, Belgium
     November 29,1924

* Came from a family of several generations of musicians.

* He is quoted: "Just think of it, if I hadn't hit on music, I should
  never have been able to do anything in the world."

* He was guided away from symphonic writing toward opera by
  his teacher Ponchielli.

* Tosca

* La Boheme

* Madame Butterfly

ANSWER on page 71

COMPOSERS OF THE AMERICAS

```
A S Y D Z W D R J D Z T B O T A U V Z J R S
G D S X G A F Q Y S E V I A D A A P R O E U
H A Y O W B M Q O O V C V S I E R O L F D Q
H G R I F F E S W H A R R I S N E I N N T J
Z L A B I E S Z G K H P S T L E T E O O D O
Y R C P I S T O N R C R G L D L R M O N N S
X B Z J S E C I S R E T N E P R A C A B R M
K R A T E E B H E V T B L I M I C L B A E G
R G U B T T L S U H L L C H D E P P O B T I
U E K M J N T E U M O E B T O O N V A B R N
M L B U J O L A G J A V G N C S P O I . I O A
I E J R N T A Q O N J N H A H X O U T T P S
A P Q C A J D I S G A R C A C O C N X T N T
U E Z S A B O F T E T C P U N N B I N Z I E
D L L I T S N A W C Y E D O V E I W P S O R
M H F H P E K K B N R S S B R P S H X X W A
B H Y N F Y V T F O A S G S S E S S I O N S
V X X W Y W F E M P U O B T A O M R Z A A R
D A A M G G R M N R U T R O C H B E R G S E
H X Z U E P C Y E S I P M N S H E G N E A T
T K N K Q E C D D E O F K V N U E H E I W N
F R Q Z P M O G Z G V D N C H D U T A A F E
```

WORDS IN THIS PUZZLE

ABOUT	CRAGS	LORE	RED
ADO	CRESTON	MENOTTI	REVUELTAS
AINT	CRUMB	NASA	ROCHBERG
ANGELES	DELLO JOIO	NO	ROE
ANTHIEL	DEN	NONO	SAP
ASSET	DIAMOND	OFT	SCHUMAN
BABBITT	ENTERS	OH	SESSIONS
BABY	FINE	ONE	SHAPERO
BARBER	FOSS	ORE	SOS
BERGSMA	GAR	OUT	STEVENS
BIS	GERSHWIN	OWN	STILL
CAGE	GINASTERA	PISTON	TEE
CAR	GRIFFES	PONCE	TIA
CARPENTER	HARRIS	PORTER	TIS
CARTER	HOVHANESS	PUP	TOO
CHAVEZ	IVES	RATE	VILLA-LOBOS
COPLAND	LEA		

ANSWER on page 73

COMPOSERS OF THE AMERICAS

Match the composers' last names to the first and/or middle names found in this puzzle.

ACROSS
1. Vehicle
3. Gian Carlo
6. Roger
9. High rocky places
11. Color
14. Canine offspring
16. Assess
18. Very young human
19. Heitor
20. Frequently
22. Spanish speaking aunt
23. Irving
24. Mine find
25. Negative
26. Los _____
27. Fish eggs
28. Single unit
29. Also
32. Lukas
34. Alan
37. Carlos
39. William
40. Big production
42. Field
43. Elongated fish
44. Manuel
45. Again
48. Alberto
49. Distress signal
51. William Grant
54. Approximately
55. David
58. Comes in
59. Elliott
60. Paul

DOWN
1. George
2. George
4. Space agency
5. Golf gadget
7. Tree fluid
8. William
10. Charles Tomlinson
11. Silvestre
12. Norman
13. Harold
15. Walter
17. Quincy
21. _____ the season
25. Admonition
26. George
30. Roy
31. George
33. Halsey
35. _____ my
36. John Alden
37. Aaron
38. Is not: slang
39. Milton
41. Charles Edward
46. Samuel
47. Strong point
50. Possess
52. Tradition
53. John
56. Away
57. Lair

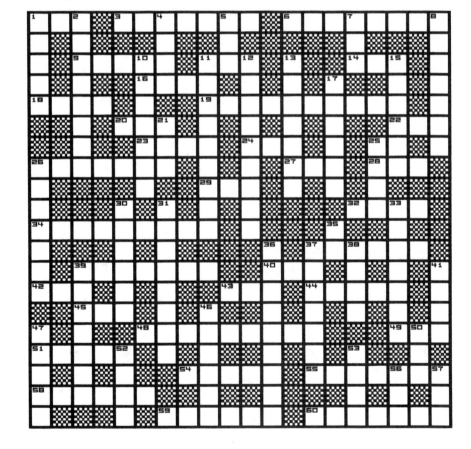

ANSWER on page 72

MUSICAL SLANG

```
Z  R  S  J  X  D  H  A  S  P  O  H  C  S  B  I
W  U  I  N  W  R  M  B  L  N  C  C  K  T  L  N
X  E  E  F  I  K  L  I  L  R  I  C  N  I  U  I
T  R  Y  F  F  O  L  L  A  F  A  P  C  G  Z  M
S  W  E  E  W  G  G  S  B  R  V  K  R  N  T  A
K  M  S  K  G  R  H  R  T  A  W  G  D  I  L  L
Q  Y  D  H  N  L  C  D  O  J  L  C  W  W  A  C
N  D  R  Q  Z  I  A  X  O  O  A  P  O  F  M  H
N  G  I  H  R  O  L  S  F  N  V  M  O  Y  H  A
D  Y  B  C  R  D  O  C  S  E  R  E  D  B  C  R
Q  A  L  L  G  O  O  S  E  E  G  G  S  G  S  T
D  E  I  V  I  I  J  V  C  O  S  S  H  J  Y  T
D  A  G  N  G  N  B  J  P  E  N  G  E  J  V  U
R  E  Y  K  K  L  E  X  R  P  G  D  G  C  B
```

WORDS IN THIS PUZZLE

AX	CRASH	INK
BIRD'S EYE	DOINK	JAM
BLOW	EYEGLASSES	LICK
CANS	FALL OFF	RAILROAD TRACKS
CHART	FOOTBALLS	RIFF
CHOPS	GIG	SCHMALTZ
CIRCLE	GOOSE EGGS	WING IT
CLAM	GROOVE	WOODSHED
CLINKER	HAIR PINS	

ANSWER on page 73

MUSICAL SLANG

Some of the slang or "non-conventional" musical terms in this puzzle are used by musicians universally. Others are more likely to be heard in recording studios or from jazz musicians.

ACROSS
1. Short showy musical statement
5. See 1A
7. Whole notes
9. Play
12. Wrong note
14. See 7A
15. Type of upward glissando in jazz style
16. Come in wrong
18. Fermata
19. Cut off; stop
22. Feel of the tempo
23. Play without preparation
24. Exaggerated sentiment

DOWN
2. Type of downward glissando in jazz style
3. Play as written
4. Headphones
6. Playing engagement
8. "Caution", watch for tempo change
10. Practice
11. Mark for omission
12. Wrong note
13. Improvise
16. Written music
17. A short crescendo followed by a short diminuendo
20. Instrument
21. Technique

ANSWER on page 72

NAME THESE NOTABLES #2

1. _____

2. _____

3. _____

4. _____

5. _____

6. _____

ANSWER on page 71

36

INSTRUMENTAL SEARCH

```
F E K H M I W L R U E I S A W G C P H A
A L O G E E V N I D N L U K S Q B F F T
P G U B P I C C O L O J N A B L R V L J
F N I G O A M U R D E R A N S H X I U D
C A O L E G B F R E N C H H O R N N T S
I I A A C L E U T N N V C L M O E A E D
G R F N E O H N T E H A L G O N P P N G
P T S B G C N O O L P E G S I I R M G N
Y P A V P K G T R B C M S R M D A I L W
P S T E V E R S R N M A U U O R H T I X
S T S G J N F U O A B O R R I Z X B S N
F E E U U S E L Z U B D R M T Y B O H I
Z N L I P P O O S M S A B T L X K N H L
Z A E T J I R F A S I A S O I T C G O O
H T C A V E V T A H A R P S I C H O R D
P S X R F L I B T D R H E H O B C S N N
S A X O P H O N E T O M D R O O I E Y A
P C U E T U L T E N I R A L C N N C H M
K A X O N A I P E H Q E Q L E O E W V X
U B Y W D K N V C O N G L N L F S N B U
```

WORDS IN THIS PUZZLE

BANJO
BASS DRUM
BASSOON
BONGOS
CASTANETS
CELESTA
CHIMES
CLARINET
CONTRABASSOON
DOUBLE BASS

ENGLISH HORN
FLUGELHORN
FLUTE
FRENCH HORN
GLOCKENSPIEL
GUITAR
HARP
HARPSICHORD
LUTE
MANDOLIN

MARIMBA
OBOE
ORGAN
PIANO
PICCOLO
SAXOPHONE
SNARE DRUM
SOUSAPHONE
TAMBOURINE

TIMPANI
TRIANGLE
TROMBONE
TRUMPET
TUBA
VIOLA
VIOLIN
VIOLONCELLO
XYLOPHONE

ANSWER on page 72

SCRAMBLE #3

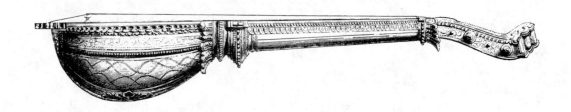

MAMARIB

LUFTE

SOASNOB

OILVIN

LOVECOOLNIL

RICHARDSHOP

RANGO

UTLE

PHONEYLOX

PINKCOLLEGES

RUNHOGFELL

JABON

BOATRUINME

HEMISC

SANESTACT

ABUT

DONMILAN

HERLONGSHIN
BENTROOM
COCOLIP
PERMUTT
RHOCNHERFN
LETCARIN

MAINPIT
PHRA
EOOB

DRABSUMS
NIPOA
OVAIL
IRAGUT
SONBOG
SETLACE

ASLOBUSBED
SONABCARTOONS
NURSEDARM
OPENSHOAX
NOHOUSESPA
RELATING

ANSWER on page 73

NAME THE MYSTERY COMPOSER #5

Born: Ekaterinoslav, Ukraine
April 23, 1891

Died: Moscow, U.S.S.R.
March 4, 1953

* Took entrance exam for St Petersburg Conservatory at 13 by showing several of his operas, two sonatas and a symphony.

* Horrified his teachers with his unorthodox tonalities.

* His music contains much satire and humor.

* Love of Three Oranges

* Classical Symphony   * Peter and the Wolf

ANSWER on page 73

RIDDLES AND SILLIES 1.

```
J E O M H D C I D S N V J C C F N W I E S
C M L T A Y L O R B I S F F C H O I H W E
T N O G E A P V L A A T Z F R S S H K A Q
W P B A Z R N O V H R Y S R X A T E T G B
S M E T A N A N H A P R M M I R N G J W X
P X D S D Y V U A N S D E N L A W C Z F X
T U V H S H I Z N S E Z T F L V L Q K L G
P T U K I D L A B O C S E R F T V C H U C
P U R C E L L L R B A A U V O L R N E L B
K U E D B O U G M E P F R A A V O X E L P
B O B C Y G S H N R T T D L H H A W U Y Y
O R R K R N O S G N E N D R A K C S X Z P
L Q A B D R Y F M S X E E W N T C V U B T
T K B V E O I Z F T R S F P C N T O H H Z
I S K M E K H A L E D N A H R N T I T V Z
D S D M T L A V G I N O L F W A Z O O S O
R I J M S M L N R N B B L S A M C R O D O
L L T R D R I I T C M B A E B U Y C T S D
X B I Z E T L P B V A I R C F H N V H A C
L W F V S K I J M E Z G U C H C L E R B T
X O E O I L P O Z R P F E L L S A T E Z L
```

WORD LIST

AHAB	DR	LULLY	SITS
AM	EGO	ODOR	SKI
ANT	EVER	OFFENBACH	SMETANA
ARE	FELL	OH	SOOT
AT	FRANCK	OR	SPRAIN
ATE	FRESCOBALDI	ORB	STEED
BARBER	GIBBONS	OZ	STINGER
BED	GLAZUNOV	PURCELL	STOCKHAUSEN
BERNSTEIN	HANDEL	RASH	STY
BIZET	ILL	RAVEL	SULLIVAN
BLISS	IS	RUE	TAYLOR
BYRD	IT	SAINT-SAENS	TI
CAGE	KORNGOLD	SAVOR	TOOTH
CARPENTER	LECLAIR	SCARLATTI	WOLF-FERRARI
CHAVEZ	LIL	SCHUMANN	ZOO
DE FALLA			

ANSWER on page 74

RIDDLES AND SILLIES

Name the composers in the clues marked "comp." This may take some stretching of the imagination or a bit of downright silliness.

ACROSS

5. Farmyard residence
7. Has had enough of Johann Sebastian: comp.
9. Complete happiness: comp.
11. Who is _____
12. We _____ ready
13. Toppled
14. Don't _____ your ankle
16. Apes: comp
18. Healer. abbr.
19. Meet me _____
20. Flyer: comp.
21. _____ fairy
22. Remorse
24. Plaster painting with no hair: comp.
26. Picnic guest
28. Who _____ it?
29. Under the weather
30. I _____, I'm Popeye
31. Plenty of material for fixing windows: comp
36. There's a redness in his name: comp.
38. Not idle, he's always _____ : comp.
39. Taste
41. Equine animal
42. Impetuous
44. Candid: comp.
47. Self
48. Seller of footwear: comp
50. Wizard of _____
51. Always
54. Maize and precious metal: comp.
55. Cat sound and a very small room: comp.
56. Feminine name for short

DOWN

1. Forest animal and a sports car: comp.
2. Sounds like a delicious french pastry: comp.
3. Builder: comp.
4. _____ my
5. Wasp
6. A cellist _____ while playing
8. Hair trimmer: comp.
9. Overcook the mug: comp.
10. Standard homes: comp.
15. Whaling captain
17. Chimney problem
18. Out of the frying pan into _____: comp.
23. Latter-Day _____ is part of this name: comp.
25. Dirty a panel truck: comp.
27. Suit maker: comp.
32. Home for animals
33. Russian sour cream: comp.
34. Feasted
35. La _____ do
37. Farmworkers leader: comp.
38. Night spot
40. Aroma
41. Winter sport item
43. Don't fly off the _____: comp.
45. Un _____ the tangle: comp.
46. With "by", a gentle song: comp.
49. In a gilded _____: comp.
52. Sphere
53. This _____ that

ANSWER on page 73

42

COMPOSERS OF FRANCE

```
L B R X P G R R E T S A D P P L K F M P U T
B Q P C A V E B W S A F V J L O Q T B D C C
D X G R S Q I D S I I R Q D U E D O E H W Y
L A T A F Z R E I T N E P R A H C H I A G E
A A Q J E R B L T X T E C D F L R L T W O C
L A U T D T A I L U S H T F D J K D A V D W
M E I D E H H B M S A R O E V S D Z S I A A
V A T I A U C E A U E E B N V P M U M A R G
D T S S N L M S S B N U M S E I R A K D D C
O M L S A C H S I N S X R A L G L O L A L I
E R A Z E H O Z K S C A F H R N G O M S S B
A P W R B N L U Y Y V M A N C I E E J M M A
B V O A T K E W P E O U P M P R Z E R P W S
D M A U F I V T L E D F K T N E Y O D X M M
Q Z E A L N N I B E R L I O Z E D N Z L O X
Z F B S A E F O Y A S I T U B L M H H M E D
S V N H S S N R N T N S N O S O B P B M X Q
P F Y D N I D C O D O N U O G G I E O H S Z
B S B H K M A G E T Z L N O M E N T F T B H
L Z C K R I P E S T E V H E R U A F T U R I
C O D X X A A K N Z A C S N T W L S I Q O D
D T G I B W S P O V S H E N H C F Q L X Q M
```

WORDS IN THIS PUZZLE

AIM	CRY	HONEGGER	OFF
AL	DEAN	IBERT	PIERNE
ALF	DEBUSSY	JOLIVET	POULENC
AMS	DELIBES	LA	PROM
ARE	DINDY	LALO	QUITS
AS	DOE	LECLAIR	RAMEAU
ASTER	DORMS	LEERING	RAVEL
AT	DUE	LETS	ROTE
ATE	DUKAS	LIT	ROUSSEL
BEAN	FAURE	MARTINON	SAINT-SAENS
BERLIOZ	FIX	MASSENET	SASH
BIZET	FRANCAIX	MEN	SATIE
BOULEZ	FREE	MESH	SIT
CHABRIER	GO	MESSIAEN	SON
CHARPENTIER	GODARD	MILHAUD	TOME
CHAUSSON	GOUNOD	NEEDLE	TUNE
COUPERIN	GRAM	ODE	VETS

ANSWER on page 74

COMPOSERS OF FRANCE

Match the composers' last names to the first and/or middle names found in this puzzle.

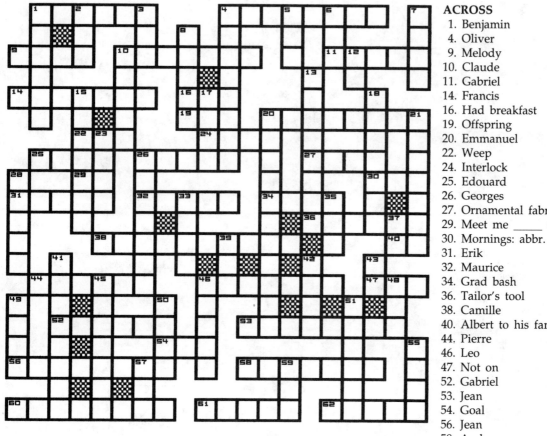

ACROSS

1. Benjamin
4. Oliver
9. Melody
10. Claude
11. Gabriel
14. Francis
16. Had breakfast
19. Offspring
20. Emmanuel
22. Weep
24. Interlock
25. Edouard
26. Georges
27. Ornamental fabric band
29. Meet me _____ eight thirty
30. Mornings: abbr.
31. Erik
32. Maurice
34. Grad bash
36. Tailor's tool
38. Camille
40. Albert to his family
44. Pierre
46. Leo
47. Not on
52. Gabriel
53. Jean
54. Goal
56. Jean
58. Andre
60. Arthur
61. Jacques
62. Gives up

DOWN

1. Charles
2. Give the devil his _____
3. Female animal
4. Jules
5. _____ down
6. Alfred to his friends
7. Unfettered
8. Paul
10. Vincent
12. _____ I was saying
13. Ernest
15. Jean Marie
17. Heavy volume
18. Darius
20. Gustave
21. Albert
23. By imitation
26. Hector

28. Flower
33. Animal docs
35. Adult males
37. Sol _____ ti
39. We _____ climbing
41. Francois
42. Legume
43. Leave
45. Looking evilly
46. Student quarters
48. Repair
49. Small amount
50. Campus official
51. Jean Philippe
55. Allows
57. Poem
59. Started the fire

ANSWER on page 73

NOTABLE STORY PART #3

sp __ i __ l __ r. _____ w __ sh ____ his h __ n __ s __ n __

____ or __ he ____ rly _____ his way to his pl ___ __ at the ta __ l __.

____ w __ s in _____ oo __ n ____ ___ nt boy, just ___ __ s __ nt min ___ __

at times. He was __ w __ r __ that he n _____ to __ i ___ by ___ mily rules __ n ___ ___ on

time. He w __ nt ___ __ to _____ about the rules, but __ i ____ his time. His brother J ___ ___, _____ __

__ l __ v __ n ____ r __ n _____ him on from the moment he got home, but

Continued on page 51

NAME THE MYSTERY COMPOSER #6

Born: Brooklyn, New York, U.S.A.
    September 26, 1898

Died: Hollywood, California U.S.A.
    July 11, 1937

* Great Tin Pan Alley success by his early 20s, writing popular music, Broadway shows and Hollywood film scores.

* Pioneered in gaining recognition of jazz as "serious" music, merging jazz and symphonic genres.

* Porgy and Bess

* An American in Paris

* Rhapsody in Blue

ANSWER on page 73

COMPOSERS OF GREAT BRITAIN

```
X S R Z Z E H S I P R V P K P J H N U J A U
C H X E Y G E R M A N Y P M H O V B T G R O
Z C R G E E O A R A G L E A N E Y T S I L L
F A J P F Z E T E R I C O N N V E B M S D D
K T N L R B S O V S F L N A T P S L I S O Y
S T A L L I S N E Y T U L V P Q T S S E Y C
T B P L A S R I I N E T T I R B U Y M L P I
E O K U T N P G Y P B A T L W B N I T P U D
R C K R B I O H K A S L T L N N S S L L R J
F A Q N L L T T X S T L I U Q T A O O T C O
F J S L D K E G L Q Z A V S A L T H K S E U
H A X T L I F S H A O V M R S A Q A G L L R
J W L L R L B I S W W D N A L E R I M U L Z
G T R B J X L R E P V O L H Z S B T S Q A F
U T J U Y E W G I L L V J K U B Z A Y R M V
X W O H H W I L V D D L R I O Y B D T Y B L
B N N C R H C U A A G S L N K N X S E E E E
O O C L P S Y Y D U A E S U P R L L E N R A
W K Y K R G Q S S E D T G P B O R O E R T N
S I R R K C V W X V L O I A H O D Y Y A H E
N N S A C T P A L I O N F A M R A H S E K H
S A S G J T O M M L G R R R M Q B P A M W O
```

WORDS IN THIS PUZZLE

AL	DAB	JACOB	QUILTER
ARNE	DAVIES	LAMBERT	QUILTS
ARNELL	DELIUS	LASTLY	RN
ARNOLD	EAT	LEAN	SOS
ARTY	EELS	LESS	SPINS
AYE	ELGAR	LION	STUNS
BALFE	EVE	LIP	SUB
BAX	FIELD	LIST	SULLIVAN
BEAM	GERMAN	LIVE	TALLIS
BLESS	GIBBONS	LUTYENS	TAM
BLISS	GOT	MAT	TIPPETT
BRIDGE	HARM	MORLEY	TONIGHT
BRIE	HOLST	NOTES	TOP
BRITTEN	HOW	OUR	TSAR
BULL	INS	PAL	VAUGHAN WILLIAMS
CHUB	IRELAND	PLOT	VENAL
CLIP	IS	PURCELL	WALTON

ANSWER on page 74

COMPOSERS OF GREAT BRITAIN

Match the composers' last names to the first and/or middle names found in this puzzle.

ACROSS

1. John
3. Michael
9. Thomas
10. Michael
11. Important to wind players
13. Pad
18. Pat
19. Ralph
24. Peter Maxwell
26. Gordon
27. Fewer
28. Cut off
29. Obtained
30. Powerful ruler
32. Elected officials
33. Gustav
34. King of the forest

35. This evening
39. Affirmative vote
41. Albert to friends
43. Thomas
44. Edward
46. Corruptible
48. Roger
51. French cheese
53. Benjamin
54. Below
56. Slippery aquatic creatures
57. Malcolm
59. Writes down
61. Finally
62. Thomas
63. Arthur

DOWN

1. Ray
2. Slender
4. John
5. Chum
6. Highest point
7. Conspire
8. John
9. Beret
12. Orlando
14. Henry
15. Fresh water fish
16. Reside
17. Consecrate
20. William
21. Roster
22. Exists
23. Arthur
25. Twirls
31. Affectedly artistic
33. "_____ to" book
36. Do damage to
37. Elisabeth
38. Frederick
40. The night before
42. Constant
44. Enjoy a meal
45. Edward
47. Richard
48. Makes bed covers
49. Frank
50. Shocks
52. Important hospital employee: abbr.
55. Arnold
58. Let's put _____ heads together
60. Emergency signal

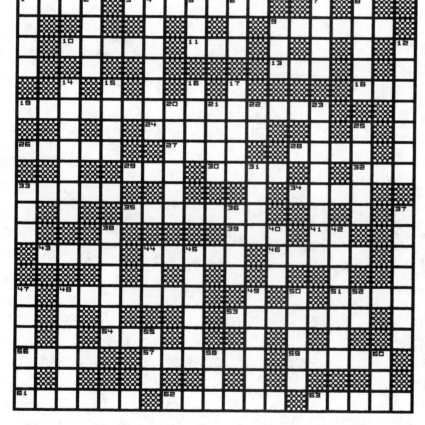

ANSWER on page 73

BITS AND PIECES #2

```
M F A N D I G G M Z X L T A A Y W T J I X S
P E T E R A N D T H E W O L F Q F F A O J
H H A L G E T W O R L D I R U K W O Y M D W
J E D E I E H A A T W W A L L D K W O G P V
H R U D A R T Y N H R H M Z L R M V Q G E M
A Z O D E R E N R O C E N M E I E I W Z M B
R T U U O E X P T X S P U U K R A D L J V E
E H T T G W I R C U Z T T T T P E M G L E G
U N I O K H R H L L O Z H U E N U H W P A T
R J S M T I F A S L E R R G N S G Q E D J A
A U G O Z T T P G R E E T X I F U V D H G K
L R S Y N E W S S E X T H K P L F S R S C X
S R T S T P E O L H C D N A S I N H P A D S
D T N N L E N D S N O S A E S R U O F D F F
V A I O N A B Y N O H P M Y S H D E O P W X
F U O N T C N I I L A A H U P A I Q X M Q A
Q Q D A R O H N L D E C I N C T Y P G E I G
N X U L A C F B A L A R G K K H A S N U Z Q
N C N P V K T L I N S I R E J W W Z S D C A
M L O R T H L U N A E T F C A H L D X E M C
U N P O M O L E H C S L S Z L G O Y P Z A V
I G G E I D X D C D L I M K K E A U O E B S
```

WORDS IN THIS PUZZLE

ADDS	FIT	PERIL	SYMPHONY
AGE	FOUR SEASONS	PETER AND THE WOLF	TEA
AND	FUGUE	PINE	TELL
ANNEX	GOOF	PLAN	TEX
ARE	HAT	PO	THE
ART	IRE	QUINTET	THREE
BILLS	KREUTZER SONATA	RAG	TIE
CORNERED	LUDMILLA	RAH	TROUT
DAPHNIS AND CHLOE	MOONLIGHT SONATA	RHAPSODY IN BLUE	URAL
DATA	NEW	ROUGH	USE
DOTE	NICE	RUSSLAN	UTE
EASE	NOT	SAYS	WHITE PEACOCK
ED	ODD	SCHEHEREZADE	WILLIAM
EGOS	OF	SCHELOMO	WORLD
ERR	OVERTURE	SO	YAWL

ANSWER on page 74

49

BITS AND PIECES #2

Find the names of the well known pieces of music suggested by the clues.

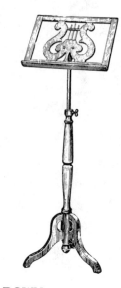

ACROSS

1. See 6A,24D
3. Fishy piece. See 18A: Schubert
6. Glinka's folk tale. See 1A,24D.
9. Arabian Nights: Rimsky-Korsakov
13. Yearn
16. Headwear. See 28A,18D: DeFalla
17. Joshua _____ the battle
18. See 3A
19. Man from Amarillo
22. _____ weed
23. Danger
26. Put to good _____
27. Cheer
28. See 16A,18D
29. Era
31. We _____ climbing
32. To over indulge

33. River flowing into the Adriatic
34. _____ be it
35. Beethoven's after dark music for piano
37. See 12D,17D,54D
38. Archer tale. See 21D,43D: Rossini
39. Selves
40. With the greatest of _____
42. Two masted sailing vessel
46. American experience. See 48A,44D: Dvorak
48. See 46A,44D
50. Money demands
51. Musical calendar: Vivaldi
53. Native American
55. Russian mountain range
56. Ravel's 2 first names piece. 3wds

DOWN

2. Pleasant
4. _____ for two
5. Bind
7. Attach
8. Bird of a certain hue. 2 wds: Griffes
10. Goof
11. Information
12. See 37A,17D,54D
13. Prokofiev's musical story
14. Anger
15. Short for Edmund
17. Masterful musical treatise. See 37A,12D,54D: Bach
18. See 16A,28A
20. King of Israel: Bloch
21. See 38A,43D
22. Music of a certain hue: Gershwin
24. See 1A,6A
25. Beethoven named this for a well known violin teacher. 2 wds.
30. Miscalculate
36. Believe it or _____
41. So he _____
43. See 38A,21D
44. See 46A,48A
45. Totals
47. Make preparations
49. Unsmooth
52. Noneven
54. See 37A,12D,17D

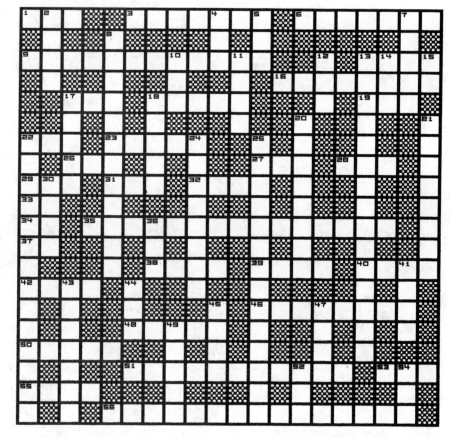

ANSWER on page 73

50

NOTABLE STORY PART #4

Continued on page 62

51

NAME THE MYSTERY COMPOSER #7

Born: Saint-Germain-en-Laye, France
August 22, 1862

Died: Paris, France
March 25, 1918

* Entered the Paris Conservatory at eleven, even though his father wanted him to be a sailor.

* Shocked his teachers with his ingenious, daring chords and harmonies.

* Is considered the leading impressionistic composer, but disliked the term "Impressionism."

* Pelleas et Melisande

* The Afternoon of a Faun   * The Sea (La Mer)

ANSWER on page 74

IN THE MUSICAL WORLD

```
O Z R L S L A T N E D I C C A N K V A D B W H S
P T L C I M P R E S S I O N I S M P R E L U D E
E Z T E T R A U Q E T O N Y E K H Q S U R O H C
R N C E A R E P O O L T C I N O H P O M O H A N
E D I P R N S F W O T N E M A T R O P C T V T A
T A D L I B I T U M C H R O M A T I C G E H P U
T C Q D R N I T C O U N T E R P O I N T C A R N
A C A H D E O L A M M N M E L O D Y X C O Y O A
T E R N N W G I E N I B A R O Q U E O J N I J F
E N P T T M A E T T O N S E M W M N R A T K E G
R T E H G A Z L L P Z S T W F U C H A I E W C Y
U U G M O C T E T Y I U E E S E K Y S L M S T T
T A G X I V P A X Z D R R I R E J O S S P O I I
R T I I G N M K F E U H C T Y P P B A L O I O L
E I O K G M A C F T S I O S M S R N I H R M N A
V O P V E F B P A V A G I U N C B E A X A P E N
O N R C F G M N M N R G S A K A D F T W R R U O
B L O O L R G Z S O N I R W D E R Y H A Y O Z T
B W G N O I U H S A C T U O R K T T P E T V I E
L O R C S C I S T A K C H A M B E R M U S I C C
I T A E D P O U L R O M A N T I C B H G N S O H
G R M R R Q R I O V N Z A A O B R A V U R A H N
A I M T O E T E L O E G A L F F R M E F R T R I
T O U O H Y N O H P M Y S X T M D I V I S I Q Q
O G S H C L U P B E A T A N O S O R D I N O L U
N O I T A P O C N Y S J P N C E L B M E S N E E
E E C N E D A C O E E L Y T S W H C A K Z L D T
```

WORDS IN THIS PUZZLE

ACCENTUATION
ACCIDENTALS
ACCOMPANIMENT
AD LIBITUM
ARPEGGIO
ASSAI
BAROQUE
BRAVURA
CADENCE
CANTATA
CHAMBER MUSIC
CHORDS
CHORUS
CHROMATIC
CONCERTMASTER
CONCERTO

CONCERTO GROSSO
CONTEMPORARY
COUNTERPOINT
DIVISI
ENSEMBLE
ETUDE
FLAGEOLET
FUGUE
HARMONY
HOMOPHONIC
IMPRESSIONISM
IMPROVISATION
INTERPRETATION
KEYNOTE
KEY SIGNATURE
LEGERLINE

LIBRETTO
LIEDER
MELODY
MUSICALITY
MUSICIANSHIP
NUANCES
OBBLIGATO
OCTET
OPERA
OPERETTA
OVERTURE
PORTAMENTO
PRELUDE
PROGRAM MUSIC
PROJECTION
QUARTET

ROMANTIC
SOLFEGGIO
SONATA
SONATINA
SORDINO
STYLE
SYMPHONY
SYNCOPATION
TECHNIQUE
TIME SIGNATURE
TONALITY
TRANSCRIPTION
TRANSPOSITION
UPBEAT
WALTZ

ANSWER on page 76

SCRAMBLE #4

NATTYOIL
ORSUCH
MINORCAT
IBEMARCSCHUM
MISSINSEMIPRO
CRAMNOPOETRY
GUUFE

VIPISAMONITOR
SENATEIRKGUY

QUOBEAR
TOYKNEE
RANTINTROPICS
BAGTOBOIL
BUILTAMID
SNOOPYANTIC

VARBAUR
IFLOGEGOS
POETONTRAM
LESYT

HOCDSR
HYMNOAR
OPERAGIG
ICELANDCATS

54

DUETE
CHINSAIMISUP
TEAPUB
VOTERRUE
AROPE

ATANCAT
ISDONOR
MYDOLE

JOTPRICEON
PROTECTUNION
ASISA
ITINERANTPOET

SLIMACUITY
EAGLELOFT
CINEMANOTCAMP
INANECOATCUT

TARTQUE
MOONCHIPHO
ILLERGENE
ASATON
ESTIMATEINRUG
RATIONSINPOTS

ZLAWT
SCARCEMENTROT

HENCEQUIT
ASNATION
VIIIDS
ROCOCOSONGSTER
SUNCANE
TORETAPE

LEDPERU
BEENELMS
MICROCHAT
PURIMSMOGCAR
CRONECOT
REDLEI
CANCEDE

POSYHYMN
COTTE
TIREBOLT

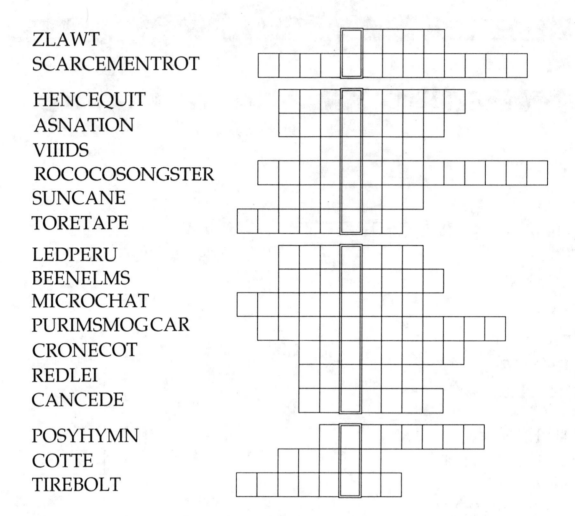

ANSWER on page 75

NAME THE MYSTERY COMPOSER #8

Born: Nagyszentmiklos,
      Austro-Hungarian Empire
      March 25, 1881

Died: New York, U.S.A.
      September 26, 1945

* Wrote his first piece at age 9, and made his debut as a pianist at 10.

* He said that he had two lives. The second began when he heard a folk tune, which started him on his lifelong search for Hungarian folk music.

* His music, though complex and personal, embodies Hungarian folk idioms.

* Six String Quartets

* Mikrokosmos, 153 piano pieces for children

* Concerto for Orchestra

ANSWER on page 74

COMPOSERS OF RUSSIA

```
A L B R J H N M L S L B E V R W O F Z V H N
Z O D E N R J X R I A Y G K I D N W Z M V F
A Q W T O W L I H Y A K A L A A H O U R L Y
Y K S N I V A R T S Q D E E I C R Y J I C E
F A A I I T E L W R A A O R I N W D R A T S
N H D B U Z Z N P Q D B U V U Y K E Y I R K
J R V I A R E N S K Y T O J L D H A R V S H
N E A T F L Z E F N A K M L V T I E T A G Z
O E K C G R E T C H A N I N O F F L Y L D Z
B O C H H C C V C T F P U M K B L K A Q C S
E T S A W M O T S A N B S C A A S Z H K N P
G F T I O K A O I K N I W L S G U S M H W Z
A A S K M H H N C L Y P A E R N Y K O R P T
D W C O K S B R I K H K R O O C C N R X P E
I K R V C X D N S N I V S V K G L I E R E K
Q A I S D M M V K R O S F G Y B O R O D I N
T K A K B A O A E B U F M V K P O K V P A S
I J B Y P K F V W M H L F Z S R O C E H L C
D W I F S S A D A P L D A Q M F U C R A G M
V O N A V I V O T I L O P P I I A J T S W X
T S I F R I I R E D A O Z E R L T M L L U Z
C M I O Z J W E R O B R V H B A P V Y G T H
```

WORDS IN THIS PUZZLE

ACE	DRATS	KOI	PROKOFIEV
ADS	ELM	LACE	RACHMANINOFF
ALA	FIST	LASER	RIMSKY-KORSAKOV
ALI	GLAZUNOV	LEA	SAKE
ARENSKY	GLIERE	LEAD	SCRIABIN
BALAKIREV	GLINKA	LIADOV	SHOSTAKOVICH
BALL	GRETCHANINOFF	MIASKOVSKY	SMOTHER
BASH	HOURLY	MORE	SNAP
BORODIN	IDA	MUSSORGSKY	STRAVINSKY
BUZZ	ILL	NEAT	TAR
CRY	INK	NIL	TCHAIKOVSKY
CUI	INTER	ORE	TRY
DARE	IPPOLITOV-IVANOV	OVEN	WASTE
DATA	KABALEVSKY	OVERTLY	WATER
DAY	KHATCHATURIAN	OWN	WHOA
DOOR			

ANSWER on page 75

COMPOSERS OF RUSSIA

Match the composers' last names to the first and/or middle names found in this puzzle.

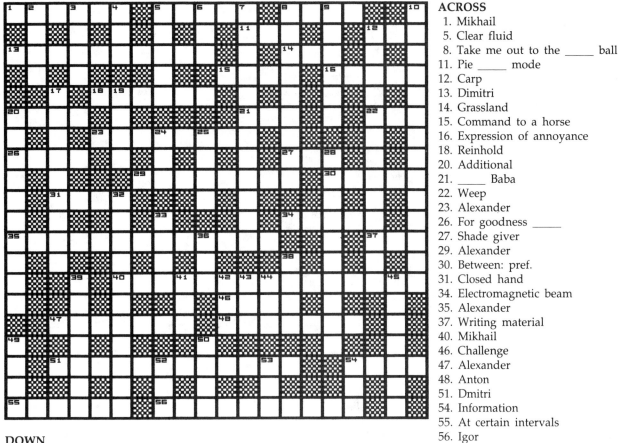

ACROSS
1. Mikhail
5. Clear fluid
8. Take me out to the _____ ball
11. Pie _____ mode
12. Carp
13. Dimitri
14. Grassland
15. Command to a horse
16. Expression of annoyance
18. Reinhold
20. Additional
21. _____ Baba
22. Weep
23. Alexander
26. For goodness _____
27. Shade giver
29. Alexander
30. Between: pref.
31. Closed hand
34. Electromagnetic beam
35. Alexander
37. Writing material
40. Mikhail
46. Challenge
47. Alexander
48. Anton
51. Dmitri
54. Information
55. At certain intervals
56. Igor

DOWN
2. Conduct
3. Tidy
4. Expert
5. Squander
6. Attempt
7. Serge
8. Mily
9. Anatol
10. Nikolai
12. Aram
17. Serge
19. Shoe _____
20. Modest
24. Not well
25. Droning vibrating sound
28. Nikolai
32. Peter Ilytch
33. _____ dragons
36. Nothing
38. Baker
39. Deprive of air
41. A room of my _____
42. Feminine name
43. Road repair material
44. Mine quest
45. Actively and openly
49. Big party
50. Entrance
52. Sales notices
53. Cesar
54. One of three hundred and sixty five

ANSWER on page 73

BITS AND PIECES #3

```
T  L  A  V  I  T  S  E  F  C  I  M  E  D  A  C  A  K  K  Q
W  F  O  Y  L  L  I  X  S  B  L  Y  N  A  S  E  Y  I  H  X
Z  U  A  V  V  A  G  O  H  D  E  Y  A  L  P  O  C  S  T  B
D  R  A  D  E  A  I  D  N  A  L  N  I  F  U  R  B  U  I  C
T  E  A  T  R  O  M  R  T  T  A  O  T  N  A  J  S  M  O  M
W  T  H  K  H  O  F  P  T  W  I  H  G  E  H  T  O  T  M  B
C  A  U  H  D  E  H  T  S  C  T  P  J  O  A  H  H  H  H  W
A  W  I  O  N  W  V  C  H  T  E  M  M  R  N  G  E  C  O  B
R  E  K  I  H  C  E  A  I  R  Y  Y  H  S  I  P  M  A  C  W
T  Q  N  O  A  T  R  L  S  V  E  S  E  L  G  E  L  N  T  I
K  D  S  V  M  M  I  O  L  H  A  E  F  E  M  M  C  E  C  M
J  A  Y  E  S  G  N  W  H  T  B  L  O  Q  C  J  R  N  Q  U
G  W  O  R  D  S  L  F  G  T  E  P  C  R  N  P  Q  I  U  B
T  E  P  T  G  E  D  A  M  N  W  M  X  I  A  W  G  E  C  O
U  N  O  U  J  R  U  X  K  G  O  I  P  A  S  N  S  L  L  Y
O  G  I  R  B  U  M  B  L  E  S  S  S  E  Z  U  G  K  S  Z
A  D  A  E  Y  T  H  A  R  T  S  E  H  C  R  O  M  E  T  O
E  I  T  W  P  C  U  T  V  A  I  E  Y  H  S  E  C  N  S  Z
L  S  X  F  L  I  M  O  W  H  K  U  A  Z  M  F  D  I  E  B
I  C  N  R  Y  P  W  S  N  O  I  T  I  B  I  H  X  E  N  F
```

WORDS IN THIS PUZZLE

ACADEMIC FESTIVAL
AN
AT
BEE
BUMBLE
CAMP
CART
CHARMS
CLAVICHORD
DAM
EAR
ECO
ELS
EINE KLEINE NACHTMUSIK
EXHIBITION
FINLANDIA
FLIGHT
HAMS
HAT

HEAT
HIKER
ILL
ION
KISS
LAKE
LIMO
LOVE OF THREE ORANGES
MOMS
MUSIC
NESTS
OF
ORCHESTRA
OVERTURE
PICTURES
PLAYED
RAH
RAIL
SAVE

SAWS
SEC
SIMPLE SYMPHONY
SONG WITHOUT
SWAN
TEA
THE
TO THE
TOGA
TRAY
TRIAL
UNO
VAMP
VOW
WATER
WEB
WELL TEMPERED
WORDS
YOUNG PERSON'S GUIDE

ANSWER on page 76

BITS AND PIECES #3

Find the names of the well known pieces of music suggested by the clues.

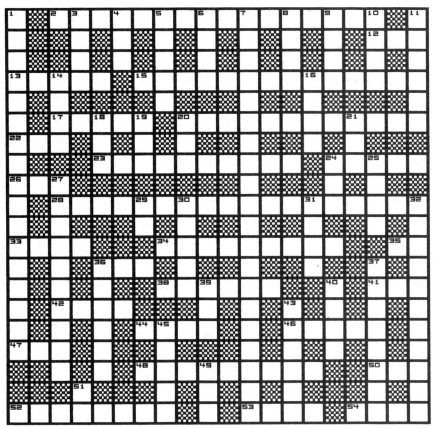

ACROSS

2. School tunes. 2 wds. See 37D: Brahms
12. Not in the best of health
13. Flyers' homes
15. Easy Piece. 2 wds: Britten
17. Wet piece. See 5D: Handel
20. Good natured instrument. 2 wds. See 27D: Bach
22. Overhead railroads
23. Art show. See 35A,52A,51D: Mussorgsky
24. 2 wds. See 48A,1D
26. Dry
28. Citric romance. 4 wds: Prokofiev
33. Preserve
34. Image of home country: Sibelius
35. See 23A,52A,51D
36. See 38A,18D,29D,36D
38. Insect's path. See 36A,18D,29D,36D: Rimsky-Korsakov
41. Promise
42. Actors who overdo
44. Large bird's watering place. See 40D: Tchaikovsky
46. Country walker
47. Listening equipment
48. See 24A,1D
50. Spanish one
52. See 23A,35A,51D
53. Loving gesture
54. Warmth

DOWN

1. Introduction to instrumental music. 3 wds. See 24A,48A: Britten
3. Shopping _____
4. Water retainer
5. See 17A
6. Sleep in the open
7. A small post sundown piece. 4 wds. Ger: Mozart
8. Food serving equipment
9. Repeat until cue
10. Long vehicle
11. Performed
14. Carpenter's tools
16. Property of maternal parent
18. See 36A,38A,29D,36D
19. Cheerleader's word
20. Spider's work
21. Environmental science. abbr.
24. _____ and sympathy
25. Roman garment
27. See 20A
29. See 38A,18D,36A,36D
30. Test
31. Marsh bird
32. Lyricless tune. 2 wds. See 45D: Mendelssohn
36. See 38A,18D,29D,36A
37. See 2A
39. Charged atom
40. See 44A
43. Attractions
45. See 32D
49. Topper
51. See 23A,35A,52A

ANSWER on page 74

NOTABLE STORY PART #5

_ u _ in _ n n _ _ _ lin him, _____ turn___ _ _ _ _ _ r

to his _ _ _ r brother.   As he _ _ _ _ _ _ down for the night, _ _ _ _ _ i _

to quit _ _ _ _ ing _ n _ turn over _ new l _ _ _ . _ _ _ _ then _ _ _ _ _ _ off

into s _ r _ n _ , p _ _ _ _ _ _ _ ul, _ _ _ p _ n _ r _ my sl _ _ p.

KEY TO NOTABLE STORY

B C D E F G A B C D E F G A B

D E F G A B C D E F G A B C D

ANSWER on page 72

NAME THE MYSTERY COMPOSER #9

Born: Kalischt, Bohemia
    July 7, 1860

Died: Vienna, Austria
    May 18,1911

* Played accordion by ear at the age of 4.

* For many years, as a famous counductor, his schedule allowed
  him time to compose only during the summer months.

* Composed mostly symphonic works on a grand scale and music
  for voice and orchestra also of large proportions

* Nine symphonies

* Das Lied von der Erde (The Song of the Earth)

ANSWER on page 74

COMPOSERS OF MANY LANDS

```
D X E R H J M R S Y N L S A R J E C I E U
L J J Q S A A M A E F F P E T P I D V C V
Y Y G Z R N R E B R A O E Q M J E D C G K
W C B I X A L L A F E D N P B S V Y H I G
A H A V T C L N O L X G D D I B Z U O U X
S R S T R E C E T S B A O T J N I P O H C
W S L I M K G Z F U E E H L I R E N T S D
Y W C I T P P I L I R T N M D F T A O L F
D J B B R Q E N L J D I A I A M V D O K B
N V J I R N I N T A D J N N Z R A P A L B
U B U X T E H U D E N S Y A S N T R G V E
K O D A L Y H C Y E I I I D A M O I K C S
V G G S T I H A B B R H T R E V A U N P S
J E E O S T U O E A A E G R D X X N R U L
M N I A U P A L N E Y K C F A E D E L O D
H E R L J B I A A B S K S K G M T U T A H
A S G T L U T O S L A W S K I S Z N R I O
P C F O S E I Y X I P R X U A J S E A G K
T O C C M I P B R K G A T B H U I D Y R X
G H A S V S L H J A Y T L O J Y L W A E C
O N I N Z Y F K F I M L J N K C C G U X E
```

WORDS IN THIS PUZZLE

AIR	DOLED	LAP	RAT
ALBENIZ	DVORAK	LIGETI	REED
ALEF	ENESCO	LISZT	RENTS
ARK	EYE	LUTOSLAWSKI	SCAN
ARM	FIT	MARTIN	SEE
AS	FLOAT	MARTINU	SET
BARTOK	FOG	NIELSEN	SIBELIUS
BASTE	FRANCK	NIN	SILK
BENJAMIN	GADE	NIP	SIT
BLOCH	GLUT	OPT	SLIM
BUXTEHUDE	GOLDMARK	OUTS	SMETANA
CHOPIN	GRANADOS	PEN	SPY
CIRCLE	GRIEG	PENDERECKI	TANSMAN
DAD	HERB	PI	TI
DARE	HUSKY	PIT	TURINA
DE FALLA	JANACEK	RANTED	UTAH
DOHNANYI	KODALY		

ANSWER on page 76

COMPOSERS OF MANY LANDS

Match the composers' last names to the first and/or middle names found in this puzzle.

ACROSS
1. Not sink
4. Enrique
7. Jean
11. Zoltan
14. Isaac
15. Curative plant
19. U.S. state
20. Understand
21. Defeated politicians
22. First letter of Hebrew/Jewish alphabet
24. Yelled
26. Mathematical symbol
27. Leos
28. Frank
29. View systematically
31. Round shape
33. Hollow plant stalk
35. Fine fabric
36. Niels Vilhelm
38. Carl
39. Squealer
41. Distributed
44. Bohuslav
46. Be painted
49. Water vapor
50. Ernest
52. Frederick
54. Shoulder attachment
55. Witold
56. Alexander
58. Write
59. Center of the storm
60. Bela

DOWN
1. Sound of body
2. _____ far as I can see
3. La _____ do
5. Animal vessel
6. Snoop
8. Arthur
9. Bedrich
10. Much more than needed
12. Ernest von
13. Franz
16. Dietrich
17. Krzysztof
18. Karl
23. Cesar
25. Edvard
26. Hole in the ground
29. Thin
30. Joaquin
32. Leases
34. Take a chance
35. Put into position
37. Pop
40. Turn around the track
41. Manuel
42. Gyorgy
43. Antonin
45. Puppy bite
47. Joaquin
48. Georges
50. Sew loosely
51. Cold clime dog
53. Choose
57. Breathing material

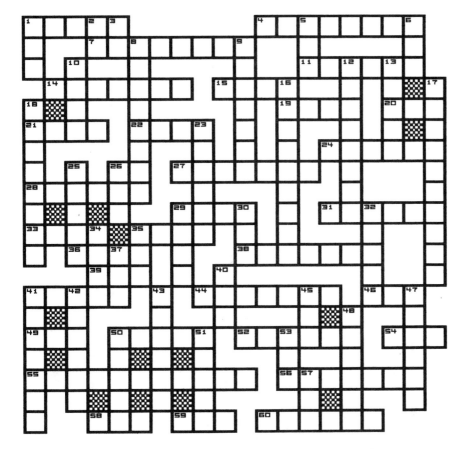

ANSWER on page 75

RIDDLES AND SILLIES 2

```
R O U T E W R F V O X C R Q B M B D C G S U
L M L I O W L A P E N I F N H E H E J E T Q
D O S E V E R D I B L O C H S J Z S T A E R
O C B X I P U U Q F S S T I C K S U X N V B
O J F J G T N K H T S E H S N Q T I H K Z Y
T Z I S C M A A Z S D C T X I A I L O D T H
L P G G I P N S T E A K A C N P T E B W V M
Z D B U S I I A L U B D C R N T C D T V L I
V J J E R L M L P L S O O C E H N X G A M L
J L M U L I R I E X I L T P M O G A E I T F
K E T I R P S I L L A T P D M N Q T L N D Q
G C O P B S I M L L M I S A Q X R H R S G A
A O U H A E R G N E T T I R B I A A D P Q N
T K K L L P R N Z W O D Y N M U E L B M F P
M B G R G S A G C O P L A N D R W R O L Q R
C R I N A M H N E L I Z A C K Y I T T Z L U
J I T N E M E L C F L L U G H D A E X Y P F
I R E L A N D U C G T E R W G E V H T R L C
J E E K T S Y L I A D O V E O S S I M A V G
H T E S E S S I O N S Q N B B L V Y M N R E
B C C E L K W O U G O N B E R X F S B I J C
H X Z D E A G P F W Q P F R F I O E S A D O
```

WORDS IN THIS PUZZLE

ACHES	DABS	II	STEAK
AGO	DASH	IRELAND	STICKS
ALOE	DELIUS	LALO	STILL
AMISS	DESK	LIADOV	TALLIS
APSE	DIAMOND	LISZT	TAN
BARN	DOSE	MENNIN	TELEMANN
BERG	DUKAS	MILHAUD	TIPPITT
BERLIOZ	EATS	OIL	TO
BIN	EST	PAN	TOE
BLOCH	FINE	PISTON	TURINA
BRIDGE	FOSS	PRIM	UP
BRITTEN	GLASS	REAR	VAIN
CARE	GLUCK	SATIE	VERDI
CLEMENTI	GOLDMARK	SESSIONS	WEBER
COO	GULL	SET	WOLF
COPLAND	HARRIS	SIR	WOLFGANG
CRATE	HAYDN	SPRITE	ZOLA

ANSWER on page 76

MORE RIDDLES AND SILLIES

Name the composers in the clues marked "comp." This may take some stretching
of the imagination or a bit of downright silliness.

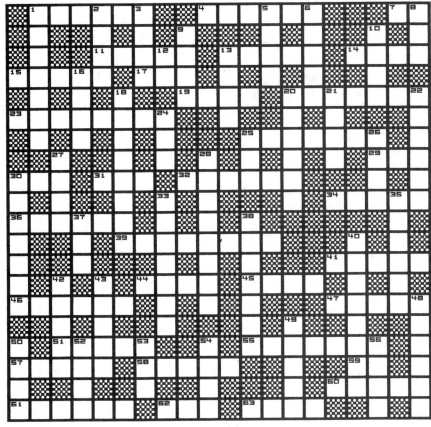

ACROSS
1. River spanner: comp.
4. Lost his job: comp.
7. Direction
11. Couch: comp.
13. Spider: comp.
14. Farm structure
15. Cut of meat
17. Formal address
19. Bird
20. Tilt it over: comp.
23. Practice or recording _____: comp.
25. Almost out of debt: comp.
29. Lubricant
30. Dove talk
31. A long time _____
32. The fellows are at home: comp.
34. In _____ houses don't throw: comp.
36. Auto part: comp.
39. Valuable metal and German money: comp.
41. Eliminate the first letter for good fortune: comp.
44. Conceited
45. Hide out: comp.
46. With the third letter changed to V, sneaky: comp.
47. Faulty
51. Box
55. Precious jewel: comp.
57. Is in pain
58. Quiet: comp.
59. I want _____ be
60: Roster: comp.
61. Famous Tweed: comp.
62. Shoe part
63. O.K.

DOWN
1. England: comp.
2. Office equipment
3. Lunches
5. Pats
6. Italian Mr. Green: comp.
8. Give a poor review
9. Town: comp.
10. Show concern
12. Roman numeral
13. Forest denizen: comp.
16. Domed part of a building
18. Animal group: comp. (first name)
20. Soup serving bowl: comp.
21. Prissy
22. Hebrew prayer shawl: comp.
24. Ready
25. Storage compartment
26. French author
27. Don't make a _____: comp.
28. Relate to a male: comp.
30. Police country: comp.
33. Reads like a noisy factory minus an h: comp.
35. _____ and stones
37. Color
38. Erin: comp.
40. With "san", a California beach town: comp.
42. Walk around the _____: comp.
43. Put up your _____: comp
48. Elflike supernatural being
49. Where are you _____? comp.
50. 50 yard _____
52. Back
53. Superlative ending
54. Medicinal plant
56. Specified amount

ANSWER on page 75

NAME THE MYSTERY COMPOSER #10

Born: Petrograd, Russia
September 25, 1906

Died: Moscow, USSR
August 9, 1975

* Talent was recognized when at the age of five, the day after attending an opera, he sang several important arias.

* His first symphony, as his graduating piece from Leningrad Conservatory, earned him world fame at the age of 20.

* Was a firefighter during the German siege of Leningrad in 1941 and wrote many pieces depicting the horrors of the second World War.

* Fifteen Symphonies and Fifteen String Quartets

* The Nose

* The Age of Gold

ANSWER on page 74

ANSWERS

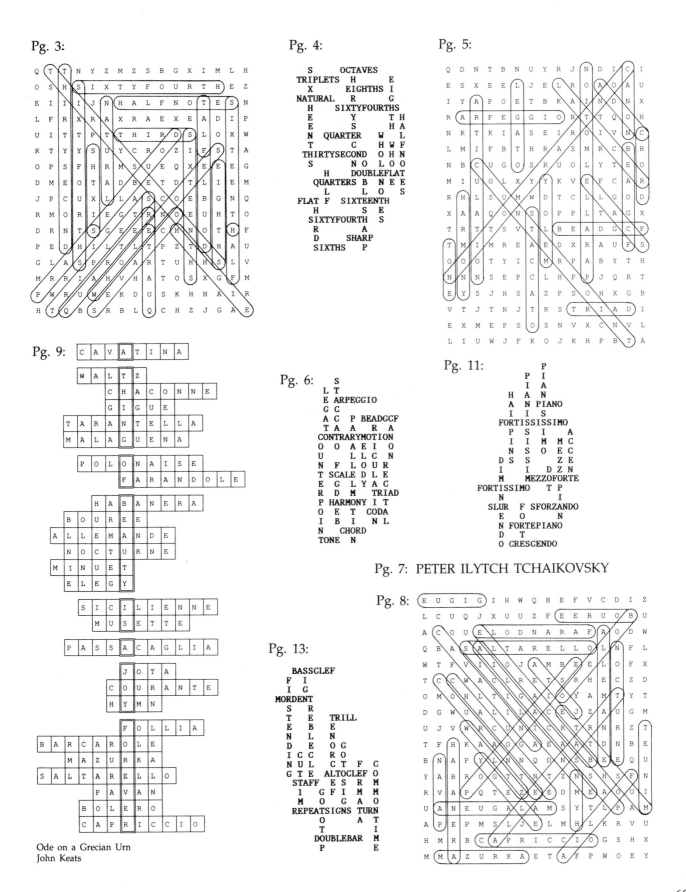

Pg. 9: Ode on a Grecian Urn / John Keats

Pg. 7: PETER ILYTCH TCHAIKOVSKY

Pg. 10:

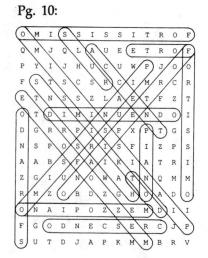

Pg. 12:

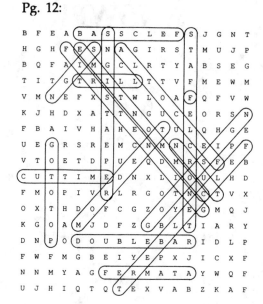

Pg. 15: MAURICE RAVEL

Pg. 16:

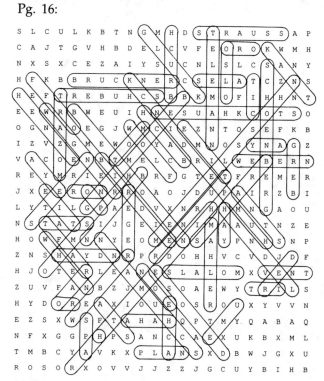

Pg. 17:

```
WHEN HAY BRAHMS BERG
  E   A    A  AEIL
ANY AYE SCHOENBERG U
  ZRDM    HDDC
WEBERN O HUMPERDINCK
O  G  ZISLE
L TELEMANN  S   M
  F  R  R DEPOSE PLAN
   BO  TIE O O A  H
O R RED  M  HANDEL
SLALOM TRI EON T E
L  I  I TOM STERN
O N STOCKHAUSEN U O
   W  C  ART  R OR
BEETHOVEN  BRUCKNER
  B UE T   A  EF
BECOMING  BRUCH RAFT
  R  ATSPAS A LA
     N  T C SCHUBERT
WAGNER ACHE  A S S
```

Pg. 18:

Pg. 19:

```
FANTASTICSYMPHONY
  L R P H  O   E
  P I O I I FOR  L
CARNIVALOFTHEANIMALS
  S CEL  ARD   Y
STOOP S ENIGMA   M
 OL  T TORS RIB P
 R NIGHTON C I ASH
 A P ENVO  TIL O
FLOOD P BARNS E D N
 S R PLOW R C O M I
NYETS A  PINESOFROME
 M R SNOB A R SUE
SPRAT E ART T SPINES
 HISTIR  IO  RTP
ROUTE S GOT III ALA
 N  H CNT  N IN
LYRE ORCHESTRA G NEO
  I S A  A   L
SORCERERSAPPRENTICE
```

Pg. 21:

1. WOLFGANG AMADEUS MOZART
2. FRANZ SCHUBERT
3. ROBERT SCHUMANN
4. GIUSEPPE VERDI
5. RICHARD WAGNER
6. CARL MARIA VON WEBER

Pg. 22: ANTON DVORAK

Pg. 29:

```
SMETANA     SIPS
 O R O L BIZET U MOP
 M I U ARE  O C A O
W GOUNOD L L PICAS N
 E E  W ALOE  I C C
BORODIN I OFFENBACH
E S U ONNAIGI I
R HUMPERDINCK M  N E
  W P E  A VERDI L
  I S   PAVE R R L
MINT BRIM A MENOTTI
A IKE OVAL U P R
SEWN E Z L S SLY
S A TCHAIKOVSKY  B
ERGO H R  O   FIR
N N O TIA ROSSINI
EVEN VIE BERG T B T
TAR E M E SHERBET
 S DONIZETTI K P E E
SEE    T S YES RAN
```

Pg. 20:

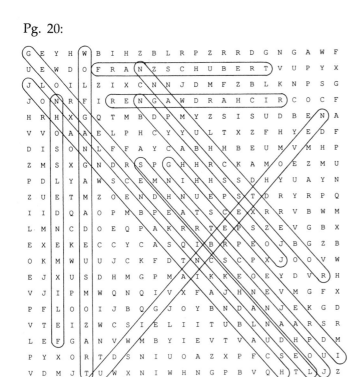

Pg. 23:

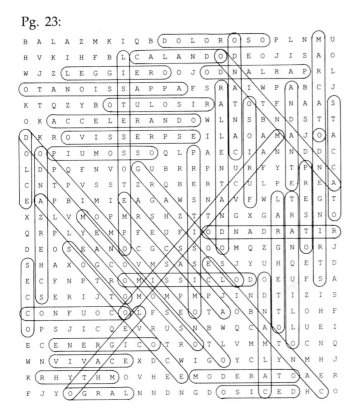

Pp. 24-25:

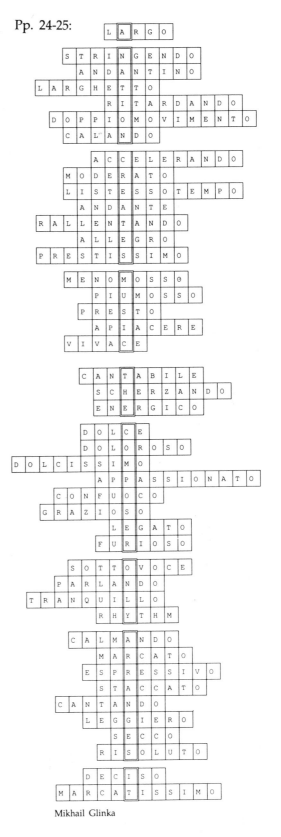

Mikhail Glinka

Pg. 31: GIACOMO PUCCINI

Pg. 36: 1. JOHANN SEBASTIAN BACH
2. LUDWIG VAN BEETHOVEN
3. JOHANNES BRAHMS
4. GEORGE FREDERICK HANDEL
5. JOSEPH HAYDN
6. FELIX MENDELSSOHN

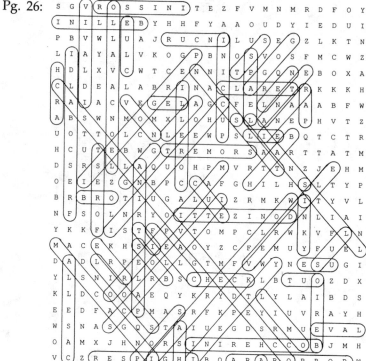

NOTABLE STORY

Gabe, a teenager and his teen aged friends Debbie, Dean, Aggie, Eddie and Deanna gabbed and gabbed till they belatedly noticed the time. Gabe bade his buddies goodbye and made a bee line for home. As he sped past a nearby cafe, he wished he could afford a cab, since he needed to be home quickly. He raced at top speed. The family had already begun eating before Gabe arrived. Because he was late, he begged everyone's pardon. The meal was corned beef, cabbage and beans, Gabe's favorites. Gabe's dad was feeding the baby egg and bread with a few beans. The baby was too young for cabbage and beef. She needed special fare. Gabe washed his hands and face before he eagerly edged his way to his place at the table. Gabe was indeed a good and decent boy, just absent minded at times. He was aware that he needed to abide by family rules and be on time. He wanted to beef about the rules, but bided his time. His brother Jeff, aged eleven, badgered and egged him on from the moment he got home, but Gabe's courage ebbed and faded. The idea of debating his needs or deeds had no real appeal. He acceded to mom and dad. He had goofed and had to face the music. He had often been bidden to be prompt. This time he had been bagged. The perspiration beaded on his forehead. Since Jeff continued bugging and needling him, Gabe turned a deaf ear to his dear brother. As he bedded down for the night, Gabe decided to quit beefing and turn over a new leaf. Gabe then faded off into serene, peaceful, deep and dreamy sleep.

Pg. 27:
```
RESPIGHI    CB OC
TN  S PALESTRINA
NE BATH SLBS
MALIPIERO STILL  CUE
AE TRAP  EIPHL
SPOIL I S LEN USE L
CNYO SCAN INCUR A
ARCH      AU  CLUE
GAW  PERGOLESI B
NOV OV LAVE SNAIL
I ALL E  AGOG TIND
 L FOREST TP LIMO
CLEF D TREMORS  N
VO ELI  IDR RANI
I  RC  LEAPS OZ
V CORELLI SOSE
ASHA A  CR SLAT
L ERR FRESCOBALDI T
DCIEO  INI
INKY OUT BOCCHERINI
```

Pg. 35:
```
   RIFF I
       ANC
   LICK GA
    L   IN
   GOOSEEGGS
       FY
   BLOW F EC
CLAM   OJGI
L      FOOTBALLS R
DOINK  D   MAC
N  CRASH    SL
K HH H BIRDSEYE
E AAE  E
RAILROADTRACKS
 RTX     H
 P      GROOVE
WINGIT    P
 N        S
SCHMALTZ
```

Pg. 33: CAR MENOTTI SESSIONS
```
R O A E     A C
U CRAGS RED S  PUP H
MH  RATE EHP  IU
BABY I VILLALOBOS M
E OFT ULPR TIA
R FINE ORE T NO N
ANGELES L J ROE ONE
N  S  TOO ORN
T  HGAI FOSS
HOVHANESS O  OT
I  RR  C CHAVEZ
E BERGSMA ADO I VI
LEA I H GAR PONCE V
 BIS WB PLTNE
A B GINASTERA SOS
STILL NR NNC W
S TO ABOUT DIAMOND
ENTERS E E GUE
T  E CARTER CRESTON
```

Pg. 28:

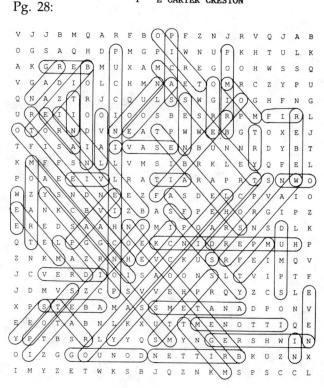

Pg. 32:

Pp. 38-39:

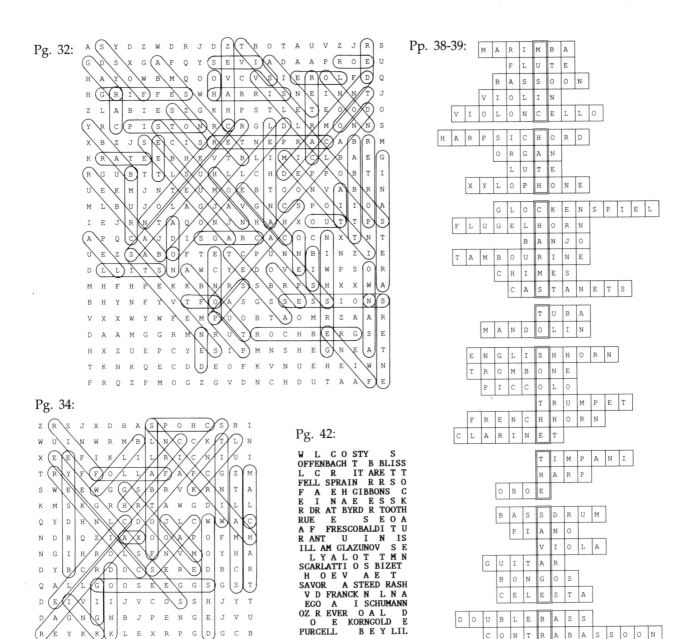

MARIMBA
FLUTE
BASSOON
VIOLIN
VIOLONCELLO
HARPSICHORD
ORGAN
LUTE
XYLOPHONE
GLOCKENSPIEL
FLUGELHORN
BANJO
TAMBOURINE
CHIMES
CASTANETS
TUBA
MANDOLIN
ENGLISHHORN
TROMBONE
PICCOLO
TRUMPET
FRENCHHORN
CLARINET
TIMPANI
HARP
OBOE
BASSDRUM
PIANO
VIOLA
GUITAR
BONGOS
CELESTA
DOUBLEBASS
CONTRABASSOON
SNAREDRUM
SAXOPHONE
SOUSAPHONE
TRIANGLE

The Mourning Bride
William Congreve

Pg. 34:

Pg. 42:

```
W  L  CO STY    S
OFFENBACH T  B BLISS
L   C R   IT ARE T T
FELL SPRAIN  RR SO
F   A  E H GIBBONS  C
E   I  NAE ESS K
R DR AT BYRD R TOOTH
RUE   E    S EO A
A  F FRESCOBALDI T U
R ANT  U  I N  IS
ILL AM GLAZUNOV  S E
   L YALOT  TMN
SCARLATTI O S BIZET
   H OEV  AE T
SAVOR   A STEED RASH
    V D FRANCK N  LNA
EGO  A  I SCHUMANN
OZ R EVER  OAL  D
O   E KORNGOLD E
PURCELL    B E Y LIL
```

Pg. 40: SERGE PROKOFIEV

Pg. 46: GEORGE GERSHWIN

Pg. 44:

```
GODARD   MESSIAEN F
O U O D A I L   R
TUNE DEBUSSY T FAURE
 N  I K S   C S E
POULENC ATE   H M
  D E D SON CHABRIER
  CRY  MESH U L O
LALO BIZET A SASH U
A  ATE   R S AMS
SATIE RAVEL PROM U S
T  R L E  NEEDLE
E   SAINTSAENS N AL
R C  OSRTB G
 BOULEZ DELIBES OFF
GUE DO EARI
R PIERNE R FRANCAIX
A E R AIM   M L
MARTINON S JOLIVET E
 IND    IAT
HONEGGER IBERT QUITS
```

Pg. 48:

```
BULL TIPPETT  P F
E  E R AO TALLIS
A BALFE LIP A O E G
M  N L   MAT L I
 P C A L B   DAB
VAUGHANWILLIAMS   B
 R U DAVIES  U S O
JACOB LESS CLIP N
 E  GOT TSAR L INS
HOLST O  R LION
O L TONIGHT V S L
W  D   AYE AL  U
 ARNE ELGAR VENAL T
  L A E M E  M Y
A QUILTER  B S BRIE
R U U  M BRITTEN N
N I SUB A I U R S
EELS  ARNOLD NOTES
L T  X U G S  O
LASTLY MORLEY BLISS
```

Pg. 50:

```
AND  QUINTET RUSSLAN
 I W  E I  N
SCHEHEREZADE  A PINE
 E I R A CORNERED
FIT TROUT  T TEX
 U E H  A S E O
RAG PERIL K C R V
H USE E U  RAH HAT E
AGE ARE DOTE E  N R
PO  C  M U L D T
SO MOONLIGHTSONATA U
OF  COL ZM H R
D   K TELL EGOS EASE
YAWL N A R  WA
I I  E  A SYMPHONY
N L WORLD O  LLS
BILLS ODN A F
L I FOURSEASONS UTE
URAL  G  T D  H
E M DAPHNISANDCHLOE
```

Pg. 59:

```
GLINKA WATER BALL  R
 E E C A R ALA I KOI
KABALEVSKY C LEA H M
 D T  T WHOA DRATS
  P GLIERE M K O T K
MORE A   ALI V CRY
U O SCRIABIN R  H K
SAKE E L U I ELM A O
S O  GLAZUNOV INTER
O FIST  ZO  AUS
R I C S  F LASER A
GRETCHANINOFF K INK
S V A A I  OOAO
K S IPPOLITOVIVANOV
Y M K  W DARE S V
 BORODIN ARENSKY E
B T V  D   Y R
A SHOSTAKOVICH DATA
S E K D O U  AL
HOURLY STRAVINSKY Y
```

Pg. 41:

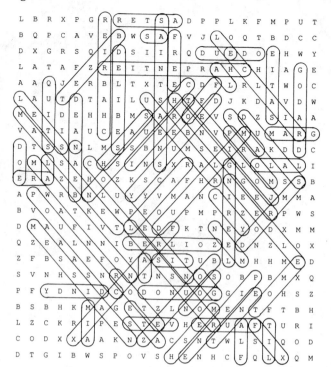

Pg. 43:

Pg. 61:

```
Y ACADEMICFESTIVAL P
O  A A U A I R A  ILL
U  R M S M N A M M A
NESTS SIMPLESYMPHONY
GA      C   K O   E
P  WATER WELLTEMPERED
ELS H A E   E S C
R   EXHIBITION TOTHE
SEC      N    E O
O LOVEOFTHREEORANGES
NA    F R  N A A O
SAVE  FINLANDIA  AN
GI BEE A C L  O G
UCU  FLIGHT  L  VOW
I HAMS    O T C A E I
D O B SWAN M HIKER T
EAR L O   U A E T H
D E ORCHESTRA  UNO
    A   D A I M   R U
PICTURES  T KISS HEAT
```

Pg. 52:
CLAUDE DEBUSSY

Pg. 57:
BELA BARTOK

Pg. 49:

Pg. 47:

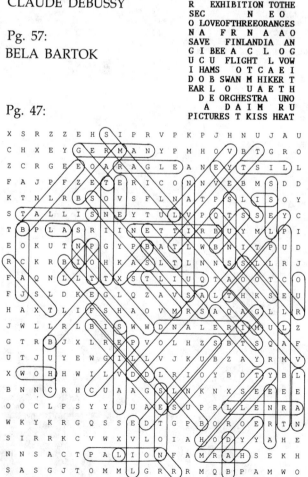

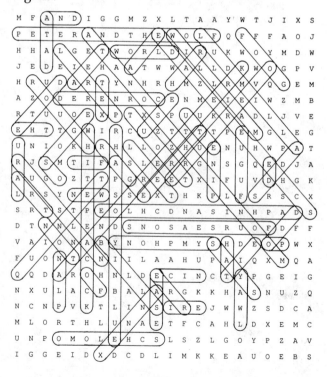

Pg. 63: GUSTAV MAHLER

Pg. 68: DMITRY SHOSTAKOVICH

74

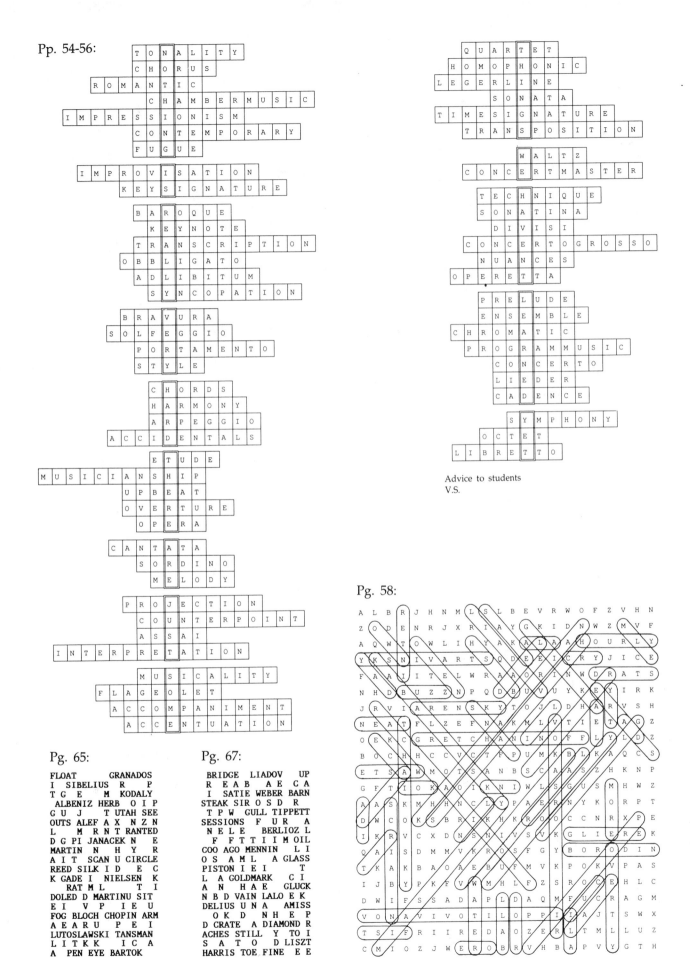

Crossword answers (Pp. 54-56), left section:

TONALITY / CHORUS / ROMANTIC / CHAMBERMUSIC / IMPRESSIONISM / CONTEMPORARY / FUGUE / IMPROVISATION / KEYSIGNATURE / BAROQUE / KEYNOTE / TRANSCRIPTION / OBBLIGATO / ADLIBITUM / SYNCOPATION / BRAVURA / SOLFEGGIO / PORTAMENTO / STYLE / CHORDS / HARMONY / ARPEGGIO / ACCIDENTALS / ETUDE / MUSICIANSHIP / UPBEAT / OVERTURE / OPERA / CANTATA / SORDINO / MELODY / PROJECTION / COUNTERPOINT / ASSAI / INTERPRETATION / MUSICALITY / FLAGEOLET / ACCOMPANIMENT / ACCENTUATION

Crossword answers, right section:

QUARTET / HOMOPHONIC / LEGERLINE / SONATA / TIMESIGNATURE / TRANSPOSITION / WALTZ / CONCERTMASTER / TECHNIQUE / SONATINA / DIVISI / CONCERTOGROSSO / NUANCES / OPERETTA / PRELUDE / ENSEMBLE / CHROMATIC / PROGRAMMUSIC / CONCERTO / LIEDER / CADENCE / SYMPHONY / OCTET / LIBRETTO

Advice to students
V.S.

Pg. 58:

```
A L B R J H N M L S L B E V R W O F Z V H N
Z O D E N R J X R I A Y G K I D N W Z M V F
A Q W T O W L I H Y A K A L A A H O U R L Y
Y K S N I V A R T S Q D E E I C R Y J I C E
F A A I I T E L W R A A O R I N W D R A T S
N H D B U Z Z N P Q D B U V U Y K E Y I R K
J R V I A R E N S K Y T O J L D H A R V S H
N E A T F L Z E F N A K M L V T I E T A G Z
O E K C G R E T C H A N I N O F F L Y L D Z
B O C H H C C V C T P U M K B L K A Q C S
E T S A W M O T S A N B S C A A S Z H K N P
G F T I O K A O I K N I W L S G U S M H W Z
A A S K M H H N C L Y P A E R N Y K O R P T
D W C O K S B R I K H K R O O C C N R X P E
I K R V C X D N S N I V S V K G L I E R E K
Q A I S D M M V R O S F G Y B O R O D I N
T K A K B A O A E B U F M V K P O K V P A S
I J B Y P K F V W M H L F Z S R O C E H L C
D W I F S S A D A P L D A Q M F U C R A G M
V O N A V I V O T I L O P P I I A J T S W X
T S I F R I I R E D A O Z E R L T M L L U Z
C M I O Z J W E R O B R V H B A P V Y G T H
```

Pg. 65:

```
FLOAT       GRANADOS
I SIBELIUS R      P
T G E      M KODALY
 ALBENIZ HERB  O I P
G U J      T UTAH SEE
OUTS ALEF A X  N Z N
L     M R N T RANTED
D G PI JANACEK N   E
MARTIN   N    H Y   R
A I T  SCAN U CIRCLE
REED SILK I D  E C
K GADE I NIELSEN K
  RAT M L      T I
DOLED D MARTINU SIT
E I   V P   I E U
FOG BLOCH CHOPIN ARM
A E A R U   P E I
LUTOSLAWSKI TANSMAN
L I T K K   I C A
A  PEN EYE BARTOK
```

Pg. 67:

```
BRIDGE LIADOV   UP
R   E A B   A E   C A
I SATIE WEBER BARN
STEAK SIR O S D   R
T P W  GULL TIPPETT
SESSIONS  F U R   A
N E L E   BERLIOZ L
F   F T T I I M OIL
COO AGO MENNIN   L I
O S A M L   A GLASS
PISTON I E I       T
L   A GOLDMARK   C I
A N   HAE   GLUCK
N B D VAIN LALO E K
DELIUS U N A   AMISS
  O K D   N H E P
D CRATE A DIAMOND R
ACHES STILL   Y TO I
S A T O   D LISZT
HARRIS TOE FINE E E
```

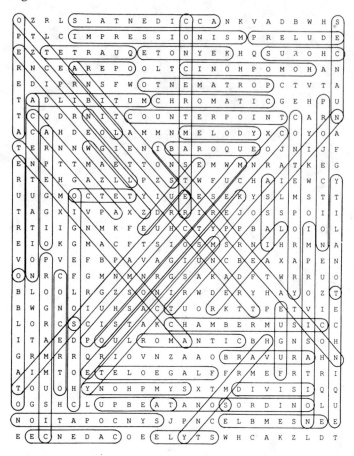

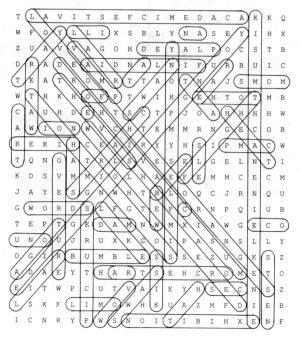

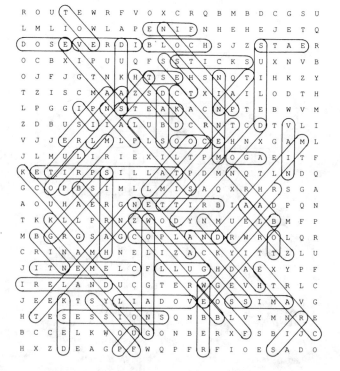

GLOSSARY

ACCELERANDO	Gradually increase speed
ACCENT	Point of emphasis
ACCENTUATION	Accenting
ACCIDENTALS	Sharps, flats, naturals, etc. other than in key signature
ACCOMPANIMENT	Support for the solo part
AD LIBITUM	Play at will, freely
ALLEGRO	Brisk, lively tempo
ALLEMANDE	German dance
ALTO CLEF	C clef on the third line
ANDANTE	Moderately slow tempo
ANDANTINO	A bit faster than andante
APIACERE	Free tempo, as you please
APPASSIONATO	With passion
ARPEGGIO	Tones of a chord played one note at a time
ARTICULATION	Distinctness of execution
ASSAI	Very
BARCAROLE	Venetian gondolier's song in 6/8 or 12/8 time
BAROQUE	Musical style personified by Bach and Handel
BASS CLEF	F clef on the fourth line
BIRDS EYE	Fermata, hold
BLOW	Play. sl.
BOLERO	Spanish dance in 3/4 time
BOUREE	French dance in duple time
BRAVURA	Boldness and dash
CADENCE	Ending of a phrase or section
CALANDO	Softer and slower
CALMANDO	Becoming calm
CANON	Round
CANTABILE	In singing style
CANTANDO	In singing style
CANTATA	Vocal piece with accompaniment, shorter than an oratorio
CAPRICCIO	Free form fanciful piece
CAVATINA	Short aria without repetitions
CHACONNE	Stately variations on a ground bass in 3/4 time
CHAMBER MUSIC	Music for small groups of performers
CHART	Written music. sl.
CHOPS	Technique. sl.
CHORD	Harmonic combination of two or more tones
CHORUS	Choir. Refrain
CHROMATIC	Tones other than in a given scale
CIRCLE	Mark for omission. sl.
CLAM	Wrong note. sl.
CLINKER	Wrong note sl.
CODA	Ending section
COMMON TIME	4/4 time
CONCERTO	Piece for soloist with orchestral accompaniment
CONCERTO GROSSO	Antiphonal piece for large and small groups of instruments
CON FUOCO	With fire
CONTEMPORARY	Present day
CONTRARY MOTION	Two or more musical lines moving in opposite directions
COUNTERPOINT	Two or more musical lines at the same time
COURANTE	French dance in 3/2 time
CRASH	Make a wrong entrance. sl.
CRESCENDO	Grow gradually louder
CUT TIME	2/2 time. Alla breve
DECISO	With decision
DIMINUENDO	Grow gradually softer
DIVISI	Divide parts
DOINK	Type of upward glissando in jazz style. sl.
DOLCE	Sweet
DOLCISSIMO	Very sweet
DOLOROSO	With feeling of pain or pathos
DOPPIO MOVIMENTO	Twice as fast
DOT	Over a note: articulate shorter than full value. To the right of a note: add half of it's time value
DOUBLE BAR	Two vertical lines at end of section or piece
ELEGY	Melancholy piece with no fixed form
ENERGICO	In energetic style
ENSEMBLE	Combination of performers playing together
ESPRESSIVO	With expression
ETUDE	Study piece
EYEGLASSES	"Caution," watch for tempo change. sl.
FALL OFF	Type of descending glissando in jazz style. sl.
FARANDOLE	Rapid circle dance in 6/8 time
FERMATA	Hold
FIRST ENDING	To be played the first time but not on second of a repeated section
FLAGEOLET	Harmonic
FOLLIA	Spanish dance in slow 3/4 time
FOOTBALLS	Whole notes. sl.
FORTE	Loud
FORTEPIANO	Loud then soft
FORTISSIMO	Very loud
FORTISSISSIMO	Very, very loud
FUGUE	Highest form of imitative counterpoint
FURIOSO	With fury
GIG	Playing engagement. sl.
GIGUE	French version of a Jig
GOOSE EGGS	Whole notes. sl.
GROOVE	Feel of the tempo. sl.
GRAZIOSO	Gracefully
HABANERA	Cuban dance in duple time
HAIR PINS	Short crescendo followed by a short diminuendo. sl
HARMONY	Combination of tones
HOMOPHONIC	Alike in sound
HYMN	Sacred song
IMPRESSIONISM	Musical style personified by Debussy and Ravel
IMPROVISATION	Composing music as it is being performed
INK	Play as written. sl.
INTERPRETATION	Way of exprssing the meaning of the music
JAM	Improvise. sl.
JOTA	Spanish dance in triple time
KEYNOTE	Root note of the key
KEY SIGNATURE	Sharps, flats or none which indicate the key
LARGHETTO	A little faster than largo
LARGO	Slowest tempo mark

LEGATO	Smooth and connected
LEGER LINE	Extra line to extend the staff
LEGGIERO	Light and airy
LIBRETTO	The words of an opera
LICK	Short showy musical statement. sl.
LIEDER	German art songs
LISTESSO TEMPO	Same tempo
MALAGUENA	Spanish folk music from Malaga
MARCATISSIMO	Very marked
MARCATO	Distinctly marked
MAZURKA	Polish dance in 3/4 with variable accent on the third beat
MELODY	Tune
MENO MOSSO	Less rapid
MEZZOFORTE	Medium loud
MEZZOPIANO	Medium soft
MINUET	Early French dance in 3/4 time
MODERATO	Moderate speed
MORDENT	Rapidly moving from main note to neighboring auxiliary note, accenting the primary note
MUSETTE	Short piece imitating bagpipes
MUSICALITY	Natural artistry in performance
MUSICIANSHIP	Skill and knowledge in the art of music
NOCTURNE	Dreamy, sentimental piece
NUANCES	Subtle differences of shading
OBBLIGATO	Essential part related to the main part
OCTET	Piece for eight performers
OPERA	Music drama
OPERETTA	Little opera
OVERTURE	Musical introduction
PARALLEL MOTION	Two or more musical lines moving in the same direction
PARLANDO	In speaking style
PIU MOSSO	More rapid
PASSACAGLIA	Stately variations in 3/4 over a ground bass
PAVAN	Stately slow dance in alla breve time
PIANISSIMO	Very soft
PIANISSISSIMO	Very, very soft
PIANO	Soft
POLONAISE	Polish dance in moderate 3/4 time
PORTAMENTO	Gliding from one tone to another
PRELUDE	Musical introduction
PRESTISSIMO	Faster than presto
PRESTO	Very rapid
PROGRAM MUSIC	Music describing specific scenes or events
PROJECTION	Carrying power
QUARTET	Piece for four performers
RAILROAD TRACKS	Cut off. sl.
RALLENTANDO	Grow slower gradually
RECITAL	Concert of one or several performers

REPEAT SIGNS	Play section again
RHYTHM	Length and accentuation of tones or groups
RIFF	Short showy musical statement. sl.
RISOLUTO	In a resolute or decided style
RITARDANDO	Slow down gradually
ROMANTIC	Musical style personified by Brahms and Schumann
SALTARELLO	Italian dance in 3/4 or 6/8 time
SCALE	Stepwise progression of tones
SCHERZANDO	In a playful or humorous character
SCHMALTZ	Exaggerated sentiment. sl.
SECCO	Dry
SFORZANDO	Sudden marked emphasis
SICILIENNE	Sicilian peasant dance in 6/8 or 12/8 time
SIGN	Marker of place in music to return to, for repetition. Segno
SLUR	Curved line to indicate connection
SOLFEGGIO	Music reading using do, re, mi, etc.
SONATA	Piece in three or four movements for one or two instruments
SONATINA	Small sonata
SORDINO	Mute
SOTTO VOCE	Half voice
STACCATO	Separated abruptly
STAFF	Five parallel lines for music writing
STRINGENDO	Hastening the music
STYLE	Distinctive features of performance
SYMPHONY	Orchestral piece of three or four movements
SYNCOPATION	Displacement of usual emphasis on strong beats. Hides the beats in tied over notes
TARANTELLA	Fiery Italian dance in 6/8 or 3/8 time
TECHNIQUE	Skill and proficiency
TENOR CLEF	C clef placed on the fourth line
TIME SIGNATURE	Indicator of meter
TONE	Sound of reconizable pitch
TONALITY	Placement of tones in relation to key
TRANQUILLO	In tranquil style
TRANSCRIPTION	Rewritten for another instrument or voice
TRANSPOSITION	Rewritten in another key
TREBLE CLEF	G clef on the second line
TRIAD	Three-tone chord with a root, third, and fifth
TRILL	Rapid alternation between two niegboring tones
TURN	Four grace notes: upper neighbor, main note, lower neighbor, main note
UPBEAT	Beat preceeding a down beat
VIVACE	Lively and animated
WALTZ	Dance in 3/4 time
WING IT	Perform without preparation. sl.
WOODSHED	Practice. sl.